The sound of A-20 engines grew loud and intense. The Japanese soldiers looked at each other, puzzled. What was happening?

The Nankai Shitai Force would soon find out.

Capt. Jim Hennebry brought his planes down to an altitude of 300 feet and then reformed them into single file. Soon they were skimming over the tree tops, occasionally rising over some jungle ridges. Hennebry saw the astonished faces of Japanese sentinels south of the trees, for Hennebry was flying at no more than two hundred feet above the ground.

Hennebry dipped his wings, soared over the tree tops and released his frag bombs. The parachutes opened and descended lazily downward. Under the trees and along the trails, the Japanese soldiers stood rigid, gaping, watching the parachutes come down like falling white mushrooms, with small canisters hanging from them. They heard no whistles of bombs, only the roar of planes buzzing the tree tops overhead. A moment later, a staccato of explosions ripped through the foxhole area. Japanese soldiers died, some fell wounded, and stacks of supplies burst into flames. . . .

OTHER BOOKS ON THE WORLD AT WAR
by Lawrence Cortesi

D-DAY MINUS 1 (1318, $3.25)

THE DEADLY SKIES (1132, $3.25)

PACIFIC HELLFIRE (1179, $3.25)

PACIFIC STRIKE (1041, $2.95)

TARGET: TOKYO (1256, $3.25)

VALOR AT LEYTE (1213, $3.25)

VALOR AT SAMAR (1226, $2.75)

THE BATTLE FOR MANILA (1334, $3.25)

PACIFIC SIEGE

By Lawrence Cortesi

ZEBRA BOOKS
KENSINGTON PUBLISHING CORP.

ZEBRA BOOKS

are published by

KENSINGTON PUBLISHING CORP.
475 Park Avenue South
New York, N.Y. 10016

First printing: April, 1984

Printed in the United States of America

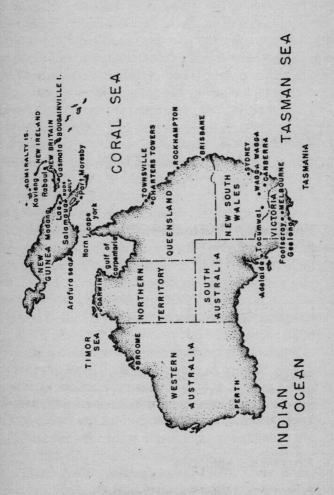

INTRODUCTION

A weird setting in a strange world: such was the New Guinea battleground of World War II in the Pacific. Historians differ on whether the Battle for Guadalcanal or the Battle of New Guinea brought a turning point in the Pacific war. However, Papuan New Guinea represented the more critical area, for victory or defeat here could save or lose Australia.

When modern man brought his war machines to New Guinea, he came to a place that still lived in the stone age. New Guinea offered an awesome, hostile landscape: endless, matted globs of jungle brush, a green cover of thick, dense trees whose foliage often blotted out the sun, impassable jungle trails, wide plains of tall, knife-sharp kunai grass. The humid jungles reeked with choking humidity, searing heat, and countless species of insects that relished the soft skin of Caucasian and Oriental alike. The sprawling tropical island was an unbroken land of swamps, jungles, and towering mountain peaks; a land of cannibals, headhunters, and savages who regarded poison arrows as the latest implements of war.

To this land came the 20th century warriors. They built airstrips next to a witch doctor's hut, where the stench of a grassy brew, concocted for incantations to native gods, stung the nostrils. The white and yellow men built their corrugated buildings for supplies and maintenance and armament adjacent to the rows of thatched domiciles where the odor of filth, decay, and disease radiated from hordes of aborigines. And the interlopers set up tents and bivouac living quarters next to village huts where the shriveled heads and the rib bones of enemies hung on matted grass walls.

This primitive land seemingly resented the intrusion of helmeted warriors with their growling vehicles, mechanized equipment, and soaring aircraft. The 20th century combatants found a bigger enemy than each other—a hostile terrain and a choking climate.

Neither the Japanese nor the Allies found a single wharf along New Guinea's coastline, not a single feasible building on its patches of clearing, and not a single road through its dense jungles. The invaders needed to bring every logistic need with them—and then fight the mildew, heat, and heavy rains to keep facilities operating.

Except for those Papuans who showed a measure of loyalty to the Australians, the vast majority of the New Guinea aborigines felt nothing for the soldiers of either side. When the Japanese occupied Lae and Salamaua on the northeast coast of New Guinea, the natives merely studied them curiously from obscure bush and then vanished into the jungle. When Australian soldiers trekked inland from Port Moresby, the same aborigines merely peeked curiously at the Diggers before disappearing into the brush.

No freedom fighter partisans greeted Allied armies or harassed Japanese troops. No one waved flags at liberators or stood scowling before conquerors. The invaders found no towns, or roads, or masses of civilians. The Japanese met no saboteurs and the Allies met no greeting crowds. All the primitive villages with the tongue twisting names were the same: Isurava, Kokoda, Aola, Ioribaiwa, Pompani, Imita, Wanigela, Buna, Madang. They were clusters of stinking huts in patches of reeking jungles.

In New Guinea, white and yellow men alike wilted in stagnant swamps, weakened on perilous mountains, and itched from strange insects that fed on the virgin flesh. Dengue, malaria, and a multitude of other diseases preyed on the Oriental stranger and the Caucasian alien, depleting the ranks of both.

Nonetheless, on this New Guinea battleground, perhaps the most godforsaken land on earth, commanding generals from both sides devised plans, established strategies, and led men in a bitter struggle to oust the other from a land no sane person could possibly want.

The Japanese commanding general of the 8th Area Forces, Gen. Hitoshi Imamura, carefully planned Operation MI — a strategy to place the Japanese at the doorstep of a most enviable prize — Australia. Gen. Douglas MacArthur, the commanding general of the Southwest Pacific Area Forces, drew up his own plan for Task Two — a strategy to roll back the Japanese juggernaut. Fate, in a sardonic whim, had forced a confrontation in heartless New Guinea, a geological misfit. Both sides expected the Papuan jungles to be an ally that would hinder the enemy and favor himself. But New Guinea showed no favoritism in sapping with unbiased vigor the strength and initiative of both the Japanese and the Allies.

By the end of the six-month Papuan campaign, both the Allies and the Japanese would be equally exhausted — like two pugilists totally spent after a vicious ten round bout. But one would be down, taking the count; the other would be hanging on the ropes, but still on his feet.

There seems little doubt that the air war provided the key element to make one side an elated victor and the other side a dejected loser. In modern war, even as in World War II, no armies and navies could really expect success without air superiority.

L.J. Cortesi

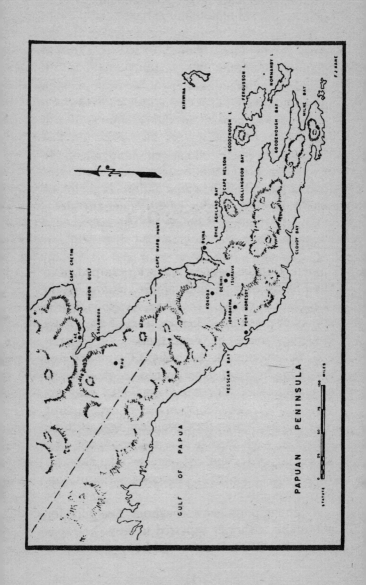

PAPUAN PENINSULA

F J RARE

CHAPTER ONE

Gen. Douglas MacArthur, who escaped from the Philippines in March of 1942 during World War II, had arrived in Brisbane, Australia, by the end of the month. When he reached the Down Under continent, he found that ABDA (American, British, Dutch, Australian) Command was preparing for a Japanese invasion of that British commonwealth. The Allied staff had fully expected the Japanese to complete the conquest of New Guinea, across the Coral Sea from northern Australia, and then invade the continent. Already, Japanese bombers were striking Darwin, Townsville, and Chartres Towers in northern Australia.

A gloom prevailed throughout Australia for nobody in authority expected to stop the Japanese. The ABDA leaders had been planning to initiate the Brisbane Line defense positions, fully prepared to lose the northern part of Australia to Japan. The plan outraged General MacArthur, and when he was appointed supreme commander of the Southwest Pacific Area Forces on 18 April 1942, he immediately abandoned the plan for the Brisbane Line.

The new SWPA commander wanted no repetition of the Philippines in Australia, and he insisted they would not concede any part of the Down Under continent to the Japanese. "We will defend Australia from New Guinea, and not from Australian soil," he told his staff.

MacArthur insisted that they save whatever remained of New Guinea, especially Port Moresby, that Allied base on the southwest coast of Papua, New Guinea, and the last link with Australia from the north.

Since the end of World War I, the Commonwealth of Australia had controlled Papua in eastern New Guinea, that vast primitive, tropical island that lay between the Japanese controlled islands of the western Pacific to the north and the continent of Australia to the south. Australia had maintained only a few administrators and a small native militia in the steaming jungles of Papua and they had been no match for the overwhelming Japanese war machine that had swarmed through the western Pacific early in World War II.

The Japanese had captured Rabaul, New Britain in January of 1942, taking hundreds of Australian prisoners in the process. The Japanese had then occupied Lae and Salamaua on the north coast of Papua in early March. They had also conquered the Philippines, the East Indies, and the Solomons. Now Japan was in a position to assault and occupy Port Moresby, the last major Allied base north of Australia.

"Actually, we had not planned to invade Australia," said Col. Yosuke Yokoyama of the Japanese Yokoyama Force. "Our strategy in the Southwest Pacific was simply to consolidate our gains and to cut off the supply line from the United States to Australia. Our occupation of Tulagi and Guadalcanal in the Solomons was a prelude to occupying all of the Solomons along the Hebrides and New Caledonia. Once we had taken all of New Guinea and effectively isolated Australia, we hoped for some kind of favorable peace terms with the Allies. But our gains had come so easily in the western Pacific that our military leaders had become convinced we could easily conquer Australia."

Early in May of 1942, Japan attempted to invade Port Moresby by sea. Five troop laden transports, escorted by four aircraft carriers and several destroyers had left Rabaul to sail around eastern New Guinea into the Coral Sea that separated New Guinea from Australia. However, in the ensuing Battle of the Coral Sea on 7 and 8 May 1942, American aircraft sank the carrier *Shoho* and caused heavy damage to the carriers *Zuikaku* and *Shukoku*. In turn, Japanese carrier planes sank the *USS Lexington*, badly damaged the carrier *USS Yorktown*, and sank the destroyers *USS Sims* and *USS Neosho*. The Japanese also knocked 66 American carrier planes out of the air. Tactically, the Japanese had won the Battle of the Coral Sea, but strategically they had lost. The sinking of one carrier and the damage to another pair had prompted the Japanese to withdraw their invasion fleet, removing at least temporarily the threat to Port Moresby.

Following the attempt to capture Port Moresby, the Allied Chiefs of Staff devised a three-task operational plan to contain the Japanese in the Pacific. Task One called for the occupation of Tulagi and Santa Cruz in the Solomons under the direction of Adm. Robert Ghormley, overall commander of the South Pacific Forces. Task Two called for the reconquest of all eastern New Guinea under Gen. Douglas MacArthur, overall commander of the SWPA. Task Three would be a joint venture for the recapture of New Britain and Rabaul.

MacArthur called together his staff at his headquarters in Brisbane, Australia to initiate Task Two—the reconquest of all of Papua. He laid out a plan called Operation Providence for the occupation of Buna on the north coast of Papua as the first step in Task Two. The occupation of Buna would forestall a Japanese attempt to reach Port Moresby by land. Further, if MacArthur could occupy Buna and build an airfield there, he could strike back at the Japanese bases of Lae and Salamaua, some 150 miles up the coast from the Buna plains.

The Buna coastal plain, some 30 miles long

and ten to fifteen miles deep, included a series of coconut and rubber plantations that Australians had operated since the end of World War I. The only link between Buna and Port Moresby, 160 miles to the south over the treacherous Owen Stanley Mountains, were the Kokoda Trail and the Kapa-Juare Track. Both were impossible to traverse for much of the time because heavy tropical rains generally made these trails impassable. The Kokoda plain lay halfway between Moresby and Buna on the Kokoda Trail, and here MacArthur wanted to build an airstrip to support his plan for the occupation of Buna.

For Operation Providence MacArthur established the Buna Force (or New Guinea Force): the 40th Artillery Battery, two regiments of the American 32nd Division, attached service units, and the Australian 7th Division, whose 30 Brigade was already in Port Moresby. MacArthur placed this force under the command of Australian Gen. Thomas "Typhoid Tom" Blamey, with American general Robert Eichelberger as Blamey's deputy. Australian Gen. Basil Morris would be the operational commander.

In mid-June General Morris sent a company of the Australian 30 Brigade over the Kokoda Trail to the Kokoda mesa to build an airstrip. Meanwhile, a reconnaisance party of engineers and Lt. Col. Boyd "Buzz" Wagner of the American 8th Fighter Group landed by submarine at Buna to survey the terrain. They decided they could build a good, all weather airstrip ast Dobodura, about a dozen miles inland from the Buna coast.

MacArthur was satisfied. "We'll send the rest of 30 Brigade over the Kokoda Trail toward Buna, and we'll send the rest of Buna Force by ship around the tail of New Guinea to land on the Buna coastal plain by sea. As soon as that Australian company completes a landing strip at Kokoda, we'll send in transport planes with heavier equipment to build an airbase for bombers and fighters."

Meanwhile, MacArthur hoped to use whatever air power he had to harass the Japanese at Lae and Salamaua to prevent any Japanese air interference against Operation Providence. The SWPA commander called on Gen. George Brett, who had been appointed commander of the Allied Far East Air Forces in April.

"We've got to knock out their airfields and communications if we hope to succeed. Take a survey of your air force and see what can be done."

"We'll do what we can," Brett promised General MacArthur.

Brett took a survey at once. He found only 26 B-17s in the 43rd and 19th Heavy Bomb Groups, 43 A-24 light bombers, a dozen B-25s, and a dozen A-20s in the 3rd Bomb Group; and 36 B-26 medium bombers in the 22nd Bomb Group. The 38th Bomb Group had yet to receive any planes. Three Australian squadrons, scattered between Port Moresby and Milne Bay, counted 12 Beauforts, 12 Beaufighters, 15 A-20s and 16 P-40s in their aircraft complements. Among the American fighter groups, the 35th had about 60

P-39s; the 8th Group at Townsville had 30 P-39s. The 49th Fighter Group possessed 52 P-40s, but they were in Darwin to protect Australia's north coast. Thus Brett had about 150 bombers and something over 150 fighter planes to support this operation. However, over half of these aircraft needed repair, service, and parts. Further, the aircraft of the 49th Fighter Group were needed in Darwin and could not participate in New Guinea operations.

Conversely, the Japanese 24th Air Flotilla, headquartered at Rabaul, New Britain, possessed an abundance of aircraft. Adm. Jinichi Kasaka, commander of the air flotilla, counted more than 600 planes under his command, including 200 Betty bombers, more than a hundred Val dive-bombers, and at least 350 Zero fighter planes that were superior in speed and maneuverability to the Allied P-40s and P-39s. Further, Kasaka's air crews were physically fresh and high in morale. Also, Kasaka could bring in new planes in quick order since he did not need to worry about a war in Europe.

The 24th Air Flotilla commander had based in Lae the Tinian Kokutai Wing with nearly 150 Zeros among its 10, 11, 12, and 13 Squadrons. Lae was only 200 air miles from Moresby. Kusaka had assigned Capt. Masahisa Saito, a ten year veteran combat pilot, with service in China before World War II, to head up the Tinian Wing at Lae. Saito's unit included both fighters and fighter bombers. His Zeros often attacked Allied targets when the Zeros were not escorting Betty bombers

17

on air strikes against Port Moresby. Saito had thus far suffered only minor losses since the Allies had few fighter planes to oppose his Zeros.

"We did lose a few planes in these air attacks," Captain Saito said in a postwar interview. "However, new aircraft and pilots were a mere two days away from our combat zone. I could ask for replacements and within 48 hours these planes and pilots would be in Lae."

Brett's gloomy picture of his own Allied air strength seemed to support Captain Saito's comments. "The bombing attacks on Port Moresby forced us to minimize the basing of aircraft in New Guinea. We kept most of our planes at Townsville and Chartres Towers in northern Australia to avoid destruction on the ground at Moresby. These planes merely staged out of Port Moresby to hit Lae and Salamaua."

Still, Gen. Douglas MacArthur believed he could succeed with Operation Providence. The Japanese had been relatively quiet lately except for air attacks and he believed his enemy was taking a breather to build up naval and air bases in their captured areas throughout the vast western Pacific. He believed that during this Japanese lull, he could launch the first phase of Task Two with every possibility of success.

However, the Allied SWPA commander was thinking wishfully. The Japanese, with their military superiority, had no intention of standing pat. Gen. Hitoshi Imamura, commander-in-chief of the 8th Area Forces in Rabaul was still eager to take Port Moresby. He drew up with his staff Operation Order M-1, the occupation of Moresby by land, with a march over the Owen Stanley Mountains.

The Japanese Southwest Pacific commander decided he must occupy Buna and build an airbase there to have air support for the capture of Moresby. In early July of 1942, he met with Gen. Tomitaro Horii, commander of the Nankai Shitai combat force, and Adm. Sabo Inouye, commander of the Japanese 4th Fleet.

"Is it possible to take Port Moresby with a march through the mountains over the trails from Buna?" Imamura asked Horii.

"Yes," Horii answered.

The Nankai Shitai Force, the South Seas Detachment, had been under the command of Gen. Tomitaro Horii since November of 1941 when the unit was formed. The combat force had previously served in China and in the conquest of Guam and Malaysia. The Nankai Shitai Force had then captured Rabaul, where some officers had tied Australians to trees and bayonetted them to death.

General Horii, a small, plump man, with round face, was a soldier first who respected bravery and courage, such as the Australians had shown in Rabaul. Horii was outraged when he learned of the slaughter in Rabaul and he had executed those responsible.

Horii was no rear office general, but a man who accompanied his troops on any campaign. His troops often saw him sharing a front line trench with the lowest infantry soldier and they held him in high esteem. They would go anywhere for him and do anything he asked, particularly since Horii treated his own troops with respect and sympathy.

After the capture of Rabaul, General Horii had led his Nankai Shitai Force in the capture of Lae and Salamaua. Now, he was ready to move again.

General Imamura now spoke to Admiral Inouye. "Can the 4th Fleet successfully carry the Nankai Shitai Force to Buna?"

"The Allies lack the air and naval resources to stop us," Inouye said.

Imamura nodded and then handed each man a copy of Operation Order M-1, Section No. 633 for the Army's role and Section No. 19 for the navy's role. Imamura then looked at Horii again. "If we occupy Buna, we will swiftly construct an airfield to support an advance over the Owen Stanley Mountains."

"Air support would assure victory," General Horii said.

The Allied brass seemed totally unaware of the Japanese M-1 operation even though reports of such preparations had filtered back to Australia. As early as 12 July, Australian coast watchers had noted Japanese reconnaisance planes over the Buna area. The planes were apparently taking photos of the terrain. Then, coast watchers in the Solomons had seen troopships sailing toward New Britain, apparently to Rabaul. The next day, a long range B-17, flying over Rabaul, had seen the transports sortie in Simpson Harbor with cruisers and destroyers. And, on 15 July, 26 Japanese Betty bombers, with fighter escorts from Tinian Wing in Lae, heavily bombed Port Moresby, knocking out two runways. Finally, on 16 July, another American recon plane spotted the invasion fleet in the lower Solomons Sea: the light cruisers *Tenruyu* and *Tatsuta*, three destroyers, and three maru transports.

On the afternoon of 21 July, Col. Yosuke Yokoyama, commanding the first half of the Nankai Shitai Force, unloaded men and supplies at Basabua, eight miles north of Buna Mission. An Australian cadre of a dozen men with their PIB (Papuan Infantry Battalion) of some 300 native troops could hardly resist this 2500 man invasion force. The Australians noted the Japanese activities, radioed Kokoda with the information, and then withdrew into the Owen Stanleys.

When word of the Japanese invasion reached Brisbane, General MacArthur and his staff were dumbfounded. The Japanese landings had torn asunder the plans for Operation Providence. MacArthur could do nothing now but react to the Japanese initiative. He called Gen. Tom Vasey and told him to move as many troops to Kokoda as he could, and to move them with all haste. Vasey in turn called Gen. Selwyn Porter of 30 Brigade and advised him to get his Aussie troops moving as swiftly as possible into the interior, and especially to Kokoda.

Gen. George Brett, meanwhile, ordered all available planes airborne to break up the Japanese landings. Sixteen P-39s of the 8th Fighter

Group and 12 A-24s of the 3rd Bomb Group flew out of Moresby at once. The American aircraft met a barrage of ack-ack fire and swarms of Zeros over the Buna area. The Americans only set fire to a pair of supply dumps on the beaches before Zeros drove them off, knocking out two A-24s and a half dozen P-39s. Next came a dozen Beauforts of the Australian 22 Squadron and a dozen Beaufighters of the Australian 75 Squadron. But the Aussies fared no better. They lost seven planes to ack-ack and Zeros while doing minimal damage to the Japanese beachhead.

Brett now ordered the heavier bombers in northern Australia to stage out of Moresby and attack the invasion site. The Americans could only muster six B-17s of the 43rd Bomb Group and ten B-26s of the 22nd Bomb Group. The bombers arrived over Buna late in the afternoon of 21 July. But resistance from Japanese anti-aircraft and Zero fighter planes was so intense that the bombers scored only one hit on a small transport before they were driven off with the loss of two B-26s and damage to four more aircraft.

Throughout the night of 21 and 22 July, the Japanese unloaded men and supplies unmolested. On the morning of 22 July, Far East Air Forces conducted a go-for-broke aerial effort against Buna. But the all-out effort only included six heavy bombers, ten medium bombers, and ten light bombers, along with 12 P-39s from the 8th Fighter Group and 12 P-40s from the Australian 75 Squadron. The Allied planes again met heavy ack-ack fire and swarms of Captain Saito's

Zeros from the Tinian Wing. The Allies only set fire to a pair of supply dumps, but they did sink a maru transport. However, Japanese troops and supplies had already been unloaded from the vessel.

Of the planes that struck Buna on 22 July, the Japanese had shot down two B-26s of the 22nd Bomb Group, five A-24s and B-25s of the 3rd Bomb Group, and six P-40s of the Australian 75 Squadron. Dense afternoon clouds had settled over Port Moresby by the time the last plane of the tattered Allied air units touched down. The fighter pilots and bomber crews told grim tales of the heavy opposition at Buna by the Japanese.

"There were just too many Zeros," said Sgt. Richard Olson, a B-26 gunner. "We couldn't do much. Where the hell is the rest of our air force?"

Unfortunately, most of the Far East Air Forces aircraft were in Australia, with most of them in need of service, repair, and overhaul. The crews, most of whom were survivors of the Philippines and Java campaigns, were totally spent after months of traumatic defeats, physically and mentally incapable of flying sorties against superior Japanese air power.

"The failure of the air was deplorable in this situation," said Gen. Basil Morris, operational commander of New Guinea Force. "This failure will encourage the enemy to make further landings with assurance of impunity. I fear Australia could be lost."

Conversely, Col. Yosuke Yokoyama radioed his superior, Gen. Tomitaro Horii, at the Nankai

Shitai headquarters in Rabaul. "They could mount nothing of consequence against us in the way of air power against our own superior air power. Within a month, Port Moresby will be ours."

And in truth, by this third week of July, 1942, pessimism gripped the population of Australia as well as the Allied military leaders. Operation Providence had exploded in their faces. Elation, meanwhile, had fanned through the Japanese troops as well as their officers in both New Guinea and New Britain. The success and relative ease of the Buna landings had brought the Japanese ever closer to the big prize — Australia.

When the Japanese landed in Buna on 21 July, only the 30 Australian Infantry Brigade and a segment of the Australian 25 Brigade represented the only combat troops in New Guinea. They numbered totally no more than 3,000 men. In contrast, the first elements of the Nankai Shitai Detachment, the Yokoyama Force that had landed at Buna, included more than 5,000 combat troops and nearly 2,000 service and engineer troops to support the combat units. The other half of the Nankai Shitai Detachment, the Yazawa Force, also numbered 7,000 men. This force would shortly leave Rabaul to follow the Yokoyama Force to Buna. Further, the Japanese had another 50,000 combat troops scattered about other bases in the Pacific, ready to move on a day's notice.

By the evening of 22 July, the Allies had realized that the best efforts of the Far East Air

Forces had caused only a minor annoyance to the Japanese invasion force. The Allied air forces simply lacked enough serviceable planes, experienced crews, and trained replacements. Further, they did not have enough facilities for the upkeep and repair of what few planes they had. The meager complements of the 43rd, 19th, 22nd, and 3rd Bomb Group bombers, the few fighter planes of the 8th and 35th Fighter Groups, and the Australian squadrons of mixed aircraft were simply inadequate to cope with the Japanese Air Force.

Gen. Douglas MacArthur hoped the Japanese would be content to occupy and develop Buna as a forward base before making any further incursions into Papua. If so, MacArthur might still have time to build up his forces, especially his air forces.

But the Allied SWPA commander was again thinking wishfully. The Japanese had every intention of immediately beginning the march over the Owen Stanley Mountains to capture Port Moresby. Gen. Tomitaro Horii was elated by the skimpy Allied air response to the Buna landings and the complete lack of any ground response. Further, Gen. Hitoshi Imamura, at the 8th Area Forces headquarters in Rabaul, was anxious to prove that his land forces could capture Port Moresby where the Japanese navy had failed in the Battle of the Coral Sea. In fact, by the end of the first day in Buna, engineers were already working on an airfield and advance scouts of the Japanese 144th Infantry Regiment had already penetrated 15 miles inland from their Buna beachhead against no opposition. Both General Horii and General Imamura believed that Japanese troops would merely battle jungle terrain and not enemy ground troops as the Nankai Shitai Force started the march to Port Moresby over the Owen Stanley Mountains.

After studying the maps of the New Guinea terrain, General Imamura reached the same conclusion as General MacArthur. The Japanese should establish an airstrip on the Kokoda mesa, halfway between Buna and Moresby, to support the ground assault on Port Moresby, as the Allies felt they needed an airfield at Kokoda to support the occupation of Buna on Papua's north coast.

After Imamura conferred with General Horii, the Nankai Shitai commander radioed Colonel Yokoyama at Buna: "We have evidence from our reconnaisance aircraft that a small detachment of Australian troops are building an airfield at Kokoda. We must have this airstrip, for once we have air support from the Kokoda mesa, the remainder of our effort to capture Port Moresby will be much less difficult. I urge you to begin your march to Kokoda at once. The remainder of the Nankai Shitai Detachment will arrive in Buna as soon as possible. I will personally be with them. We have been assured by the commander of the Tinian Wing in Lae that you will have strong air support for your mission to Kokoda."

"We will act at once," Colonel Yokoyama promised.

"As soon as you take Kokoda," Horii continued, "you are to establish an advance air base for our fighter and transport aircraft for the final march to Port Moresby."

"Be certain, Honorable Horii," Yokoyama answered, "we shall drink a victory toast in Port Moresby within the month."

"I have every confidence in you, Colonel," General Horii told Yokoyama, "and may our Samurai ancestors help you in this endeavor. Already, we are developing our airbases at Tulagi and Guadalcanal. Once we have taken the Solomons and all of New Guinea, only one prize will remain — Australia."

At Brisbane, Australia, the headquarters staff of the Allied SWPA read with dismay the coastwatcher reports of the Japanese advance from the Buna beachhead, and they read with even more concern the reports of the further Japanese buildups in New Guinea, New Britain, and the Solomons.

The worst factor, of course, was air power. In late July of 1942, the Japanese controlled the skies over the Southwest Pacific, including New Guinea. Even if General MacArthur could bring more troops into New Guinea, he would need air superiority to insure that his ground troops could beat back the Japanese ground troops. But at the moment, neither Gen. George Brett of the Allied Far East Air Forces nor any other military leader of the SWPA saw any way to overcome this Japanese air advantage before the Japanese ground troops crossed the Owen Stanley Mountains and took Port Moresby.

Not only were the Allied air forces badly outnumbered, but the Japanese Zero fighter was the best in the air. Further, MacArthur had no ships or planes that might carry his 32nd and 7th Infantry divisions to Port Moresby by air.

Still, whatever the Allies lacked in the Southwest Pacific, they did not lack men with vision, courage, determination, and even brazenness. Three men in the Southwest Pacific would do something about these possibilities: a brash air corps colonel, an ex-commercial airline owner, and a gruff, gravel voiced deputy air commander. Their antics would send shock waves all the way to Washington, but their antics would also have a vital effect on Operation Providence.

CHAPTER TWO

Despite the Buna invasion by the Japanese, General MacArthur was quite satisfied with Gen. Basil Morris, the Allied New Guinea Force operational commander. Morris had wasted no time in moving a company of men toward Kokoda from Moresby, while he readied for combat his other troops in New Guinea.

Morris, a veteran of the Syrian and North African campaigns earlier in World War II, was a hard-boiled leader who demanded success from his troops. The Australian commander, sober faced and proper, was a career military man who had not only won victories in Syria and North Africa, but also had risen to brigadier general by mid-1941. When the Japanese swept through the Pacific in December and January of 1941-42, Morris had insisted that Australian troops in the

Middle East and Africa return immediately to Australia to meet the Japanese threat.

Morris had been so convincing in his proposed strategy for New Guinea that he immediately won command as operational commander of the New Guinea Force which thus far had only 3,000 combat troops in New Guinea. Morris established his headquarters at Port Moresby where he tried desperately to prepare his meager forces who were outnumbered and outsupplied by the Japanese.

Douglas MacArthur had no criticism of Morris. He blamed the air force for the failure to stop the Japanese at Buna. He thus swept out the entire staff of the Far East Air Forces, including Gen. George Brett. For his air commander, MacArthur chose a man totally unknown to the Australians and little known to the Americans. The newcomer was diminutive George C. Kenney, a rather sober faced man with never a sign of emotion in his blue eyes. Kenney had been a pilot in World War I and he had been a strong advocate of air power, almost losing favor with the Army when he supported Gen. Billy Mitchell back in the mid-1930s. Kenney had such strong leadership and organizational qualities that in 1940 he had jumped from the rank of lieutenant colonel to brigadier general. By 1941, he had risen to the rank of major general.

Kenney had commanded the materiel section at Wright Field in the United States for more than a year and he was quite familiar with aircraft logistics, supply, and maintenance. He had then won command of the 4th Air Force on the U. S.

west coast and he had organized the 4th into one of the best units of the Army Air Force. The men under him seldom balked at his orders for they knew him to be a man of unbiased fairness. Thus, since Kenney possessed the administrative and leadership qualities that MacArthur so sorely needed, he called on Kenney to head up his Southwest Pacific air force. MacArthur believed that Kenney could turn the loose knit, often balky air units into a solid, cohesive command.

Kenney immediately renamed the Southwest Pacific air force the 5th Air Force, after the five stars in the Southern Cross, and he then set about trying to raise the morale of the airmen in his new air force.

The Japanese wasted no time in following up their initial success in the Buna landings on the north coast of New Guinea. As soon as Col. Yosuke Yokoyama established himself in Buna, he sent a battalion of troops into the Owen Stanleys over the Kokoda Trail to capture Kokoda. Yokoyama also put his engineers to work at once to build an airstrip at Buna that could house Val dive bombers and that could stage Betty bombers that flew out of Gasmata on the south coast of New Britain for the bombing missions to Port Moresby. With a new airbase at Buna, the Japanese would be much closer to their Port Moresby target.

General Horii could not have selected a worse battleground than eastern New Guinea to conduct a campaign. The Papuan terrain represented a land that civilization had forgotten. The rain-

31

fall in most areas is quite heavy, often 300 inches a year. On some occasions as much as ten inches of rain fell in a single day. The jungle itself can be a military nightmare with dense, treacherous ground throughout most of the 100,000 square miles of Papua.

Beyond the coastal plains of Buna, the lush rain forests rise into towering sawtoothed mountains, interspersed with flat malarial swamps and thick matted brush that tests the strength of men with every footstep. Reeking pools emanate a noxious odor of mildewing vegetation, stagnant green muck, and gnarled rotting brush. The patches of clearing that intersperse the dense, often impassable jungles, would seem to offer some relief. But the tall grass is actually razor sharp kunai, whose blades can cut through a man's clothing and lacerate the skin.

The climate only abets the hostile landscape. The heat and humidity in Papua is unbearable, soaking the skin with perspiration until a soldier's uniform hangs on him like sewage-soaked rags, leaving a pungent, nauseating smell. The soldier, sapped of strength while he carries his gear, must also accustom himself to torrential rain that leaves him constantly drenched to the skin before the sun returns and heat and humidity take over.

Swift creeks and turbulent streams roar down from the mountains and become slow and sluggish on the flats so that stagnant ponds emerge to nourish the larva of malarial mosquitos and other insects. Ugly swarms of these bugs continually dart about a man's perspiring face to add more discomfort to the terrain and climate. And there are the leeches, armies of them, that cling and tear at a man's legs, arms, and even his face.

Overhead, the branches of dense trees interweave and become a solid mass of thick vegetation that almost blocks out all sunlight, leaving an eerie, greenish half light. On the continually damp jungle floor, matted brush, interwoven vines, and lush vegetation often make movement impossible without a bolo knife to hack a path.

And as the trail rises into the forested Owen Stanley Mountains, a damp cold will chill a man to the bone above a height of 5,000 feet. The up-hill trails that wind through the mountains are often so narrow and potholed and slick with mud that not even pack animals can traverse the route. The rains often turn these trails to muddy streams that hamper all movement.

From the north side of Papua, the Kokoda Trail winds through the jungle beyond Buna and rises into the mountains. The trail then crosses the rushing Kumusi River, precariously skirts ragged hills, crosses the Mambare River and then runs through the jungle to Kododa, 80 miles from Buna.

Nevertheless, Yokoyama's battalion, a jungle veteran unit from the Malaysian campaign, made surprisingly good time through this hostile jungle and mountain terrain. By mid-morning of 24 July, Yokoyama's trail breaking battalion had covered most of the trail, while Yokoyama readied two more battalions of his Yokoyama

Force to follow the first. By the end of July, the vanguard battalion was closing in on Kokoda. In fact, Gen. Tomitaro Horii had flown to Buna and hurried over the trail to personally lead the vanguard Japanese battalion against a badly exhausted Australian company.

But surprisingly, the Australians fought stubbornly for several days against the superior Japanese ground forces, and in fact, two more Digger companies joined those at Kokoda. They held despite attacks by Val dive bombers from Lae. Meanwhile, the Allies had mounted hit and run air attacks against Horii's troops that seemingly disrupted their plans every time Horii got ready to advance on Kokoda.

General Horii, quite irritated, now wanted Port Moresby eliminated once and for all as an effective Allied airbase. On 9 August 1942, he personally called Gen. Hitoshi Imamura, the commander in chief of the Japanese 8th Area Forces. "We are being delayed by pesky Allied air attacks. They have not hurt us but they have frequently disrupted our plans. I would ask that the 24th Air Flotilla eliminate these nuisances once and for all."

"Of course," Imamura answered.

"It is our desire, Honorable Imamura, that the 24th Air Flotilla destroy the enemy's runways at Port Moresby so they cannot mount further air assaults against us. We would also ask for heavy aerial assaults on Kokoda to soften the Australian positions. Finally, we would ask that our air units destroy the Australian supply lines between

Kokoda and Port Moresby."

"Be assured, Honorable Horii, your wish will be carried out at once," Imamura told Horii. "I will speak to Admiral Kasaka immediately."

The 8th Air Forces commander in chief now met with Adm. Junichi Kasaka, the 24th Air Flotilla commander, and explained Horii's requests. Kasaka, of course, possessed a well organized air force in the 24th Air Flotilla, with highly trained, experienced fighter pilots and bomber crews. Further, he now had his Val dive bombers based in Buna. So the admiral saw no reason why he could not fulfill General Horii's requests.

Kasaka immediately flew to New Guinea to meet with his wing and squadron commanders. At Buna, on the morning of 10 August 1942, the admiral met with Capt. Uehara Shingo of the 4th Kokutai Bomber Wing and with Capt. Masahisa Saito of the Tinian Fighter Wing. Also present were the squadron commanders of the two 24th Flotilla wings.

"I must first congratulate all of you on your fine work during this campaign," Kasaka told his assembled wing and squadron leaders. "Your excellent air support has enabled General Horii's troops to make rapid progress over the Owen Stanley Mountains. The Yokoyama Force of the Nankai Shitai Detachment now stands before the prize of Kokoda. The honorable Horii has requested a major effort by the 24th Air Flotilla to assure the capture of Kokoda as soon as possible so that General Horii can continue his drive toward Port Moresby."

Kasaka scanned the men in the briefing hut and congratulated himself. He had reason to feel confident for his wing and squadron commanders were among the best in the Japanese naval air forces.

Capt. Uehara Shingo, commander of the 4th Kokutai Bomber Wing, had joined the Japanese Naval Air Force in 1934, and he had begun his career as a bomber pilot in the China war during the 1930s, a war that had proved highly advantageous in training pilots for combat, since the Chinese had both inferior pilots and obsolete planes. The sober-faced Shingo had always sought efficiency in his bomber crews and he had more than once berated crewmen who had not followed instructions accurately. To him, war was a serious business and only severe dedication to duty could bring a promise of success. Many of his crews referred to the 45 year old 4th Kokutai commander as that harsh, frowning old man — but never to his face. Shingo rarely smiled and he never joked. Still, Shingo's courage in combat and his ability in leadership had won him the utmost respect from subordinates, no matter what they called him behind his back.

By the time of the Pearl Harbor attack, Shingo had become a squadron leader in the 12th Bomber Kokutai Wing, the unit supporting the Japanese drive through Malaysia, the conquest of Singapore, and the conquest of Burma.

When the 24th Flotilla was organized in early 1942 to support the Japanese efforts in the Southwest Pacific, Admiral Kasaka had asked that Uehara Shingo head up the flotilla's bomber wing. By this August of 1942, Shingo and his bomber crews had made more than 70 raids on Port Moresby with varying degrees of success. He had welcomed the Japanese landings at Buna for now, with an airfield here, he could base his Val bombers closer to Moresby and he had a staging area for his heavy Betty bombers. Already, Val dive bombers out of Buna were supporting General Horii's troops in the drive over the Owen Stanleys.

Shingo's Val squadrons, over fifty aircraft of the wing's B Group, were under the command of Cmdr. Bunji Shimada, an ex-fighter pilot who had gone into combat in 1939 in China, with the old 11th Wing that had downed 158 Chinese planes. Shimada's own squadron had scored over 30 aerial victories, with Shimada himself downing five. He had then joined a dive bombing unit for the assault on Southeast Asia. And again, when the Japanese naval air arm formed the 24th Air Flotilla that included the 4th Bomber Wing, Shimada won promotion to commander and command of the wing's Val dive bomber B Group. Admiral Kasaka had heartily approved of Shingo's request to place Shimada in command of the wing's dive bomber squadrons.

Kasaka's fighter wing commander, Capt. Masahisa Saito, had been a fighter pilot since 1937 when he joined the famed 10th Fighter Sentai at Shanghai, China. On his very first mission under the renowned ace Yoshio Hirose, Saito's squadron had downed six Chinese bi-planes, with Saito himself knocking down two of them. By December of 1941, he had attained the rank of commander and had won command of a navy squadron that operated out of Formosa against the Americans in the Philippines. He had then joined the famed Tinian Wing that gave air support to the Japanese efforts in Java and New Britain. By March of 1942, he was promoted to captain and the command of the Tinian Wing that had then moved into Lae.

Since March, the Tinian Wing had been operating out of Lae and Salamaua, and Saito's Zero squadrons had enjoyed remarkable success against the inferior Allied air forces in New Guinea. When Saito and his pilots were not knocking Allied planes out of the air, they were escorting bombers on raids to Port Moresby and other Allied bases in New Guinea.

Capt. Masahisa Saito did not reflect the stereotype snob or egocentric of many Samurai officers. He demanded respect and obedience, true. And while Saito showed an air of reserve and dignity, he did not show any of the class consciousness of many other Japanese officers. Saito held a deep sympathy for his men. During an air attack, he made certain that every man at Lae was safely sheltered before he worried about himself. He fought aggressively enough, but when he weighed a decision to continue or to quit a fight, his main concern was the safety of his pilots. He felt no shame in breaking off combat if such a course saved his pilots to fight another day. Capt. Masahisa Saito had earned the respect of every man in his wing.

Saito would lead scores of fine pilots and lose many of them during four years of war. He himself would fly more than 200 combat missions, but miraculously, he would survive the war without a scratch.

Now, on this 10 August 1942 morning, Captain Shingo, Captain Saito and their squadron leaders listened to Admiral Kasaka and watched the 24th Air Flotilla commander pin a map on the wall behind him. They leaned forward when Kasaka turned to them once more.

"Here is Kokoda, a mere eighty miles from our new Buna air base," Kasaka lowered his pointer, "and here, as you know, is the huge enemy base at Port Moresby, a mere one hundred sixty air miles from Buna. Over this stretch of the Kokoda Trail," he ran a finger on a jagged line on the map between Moresby and Kokoda, "is the enemy supply route. They have been sending supplies over this portion of the Kokoda Trail and they have also been sending reinforcements in troops. It is imperative that we destroy the Kokoda defenses, the supply trail, and the enemy's runways at Port Moresby, particularly the runways of their light bombers and fighter planes that have been supporting the Australians at Kokoda. I would ask that we carry out this plan in one massive air assault."

When no one in the briefing hut answered, Admiral Kasaka grinned and then continued. "Of course, all of you are familiar with these targets, for you and your airmen have already conducted many sorties against these enemy positions. So," he asked, "can we carry out simultaneous strikes against these targets?"

"Since our Aichi Ninety-nine dive bombers are now based in Buna, Honorable Kasaka," Captain Shingo finally spoke, "such an effort will now be easier. We have over fifty such Aichi aircraft here, two squadrons of our 4th Wing's B Group. We can send them to Kokoda a squadron at a time to maintain a continuous assault on the enemy base and perhaps force the Australians to withdraw even without a fight against the Honorable Horii's troops."

"Excellent," Admiral Kasaka nodded.

"We would, of course, ask for escort."

Kasaka now looked at Capt. Masahisa Saito, commander of the Tinian Fighter Wing. Saito, in turn, referred to sheets of paper in his hand and then looked at the admiral.

"We have over a hundred Mitsubishi fighter planes among our four squadrons at Lae, and we have another fifty-one Mitsubishi aircraft among the two squadrons at Salamaua. We believe we can maintain at least a squadron of fighter planes over the Kokoda area at all times to defend Captain Shingo's dive bombers against possible enemy fighter plane interceptions. I would use the two squadrons at Salamaua to maintain this constant protection for the dive bombers, while the B Group aircraft strike the enemy at Kokoda."

"Fine," Kasaka said. Then, after a pause: "And what of the other targets?"

Captain Shingo now spoke again. "With our

new facilities here at Buna, we find ourselves in a much better position to attack Port Moresby with our two heavy bomber squadrons of the 4th Wing's A Group. We will send both the 33 and 34 Squadrons of Mitsubishi G-M 4 bombers (Bettys) to conduct a heavy assault on the enemy's runways at Port Moresby. Should we succeed, the Allied air force will be thwarted in its efforts to make further air attacks against General Horii's troops in the Kokoda area."

"How many bombers are available?"

"At least fifty heavy bombers," Shingo answered. "Our A Group will mount the assault directly from Gasmata. However, our bomber crews will now feel comfortable in the knowledge that they can make emergency landings at Buna in the event such aircraft are damaged or run low on fuel. Such disabled aircraft will no longer need to fly all the way across the Solomon Sea to Gasmata. Of course," Shingo gestured, "these G-M 4 bombers will need escort."

Kasaka again turned to Masahisa Saito. "Captain?"

"We can also accommodate the heavy bombers," Saito nodded. "I will supply two squadrons of Mitsubishi fighter planes, fifty to sixty aircraft, to escort Captain Shingo's G-M 4 bombers on the sorties to Port Moresby."

"Excellent," Captain Shingo spoke. "With fifty to sixty of our superior Mitsubishi fighter planes to protect us, I see no possibility of any air interference by our enemy against the Port Moresby assault."

41

Admiral Kasaka nodded again and then ran his pointer down the ragged line on the map. "And what of the Australian supply line? General Horii has expressed concern because the enemy still brings reinforcements and materiel to Kokoda from Moresby over the trail. They also bring in supplies by small aircraft to this improvised airstrip at the dry Myola Lake," Kasaka moved his pointer.

"We are quite familiar with these supply arteries and we have been conducting sorties over these supply areas for the past two weeks," Captain Saito said. "Lt. Junichi Sasai and his pilots of our Ten Squadron have conducted most of the fighter-bomber attacks in the area, and I have asked Lieutenant Sasai to draw up a plan."

Admiral Kasaka looked at Junichi Sasai. "Lieutenant?"

Sasai rose uneasily from his bench for everyone here outranked him. But even worse, all looked curiously at Sasai for he was only 21 years of age, and he looked too young to be a squadron commander. Still, Sasai took a deep breath to calm himself and he then bowed before the 24th Flotilla commander.

The 10 Squadron leader had shown a remarkable skill in handling an aircraft since he first became a pilot at age 19. In the cockpit, he seemed welded to the plane, as though he were part of the machine. He seemingly subordinated everything to his fighting function, and his ability made him a dangerous opponent. Young Sasai had never scored as high as some of the other pilots in the

Tinian Wing, but the leader of 10 Squadron was a dedicated, capable man who could bring out the best in other pilots with his confidence and courage. Inevitably then, he became a squadron leader at quite an early age. Still, Sasai's pilots rarely saw Sasai as a youngster, but as a man with excellent tactical ability. So they followed him anywhere.

"Honorable Admiral," Sasai said to his flotilla commander, "I thank you for this opportunity to speak." He referred to some notes in his hands. "We of ten Squadron have concluded that the best method to break the Australian supply line is to destroy the bamboo bridges at Templeton's Crossing, twenty miles south of Kokoda. Such a loss will deny the Australians any access across the Mambare River and so reinforcements will not be able to come to the aid of their fellow troops at Kokoda. Further, once we have destroyed these bridges, we can continue to keep them down before the Australians can repair them. Also if we destroy the enemy's landing field at the dry Myola Lake bed, they will not be able to fly in supplies, even with their smallest aircraft. Finally, it is our plan to seek out and destroy any supply dumps or troop concentrations that we find along the trail."

Admiral Kasaka looked at the map, studying the area between Kokoda and Port Moresby. He then pursed his lips and tapped two places on the chart with his finger before he turned to Lieutenant Sasai. "I am not so certain about your plans to deal with the enemy supply line," the admiral said. "It is my understanding that a steep, narrow trail winds around the mountains in this area, Manari," he tapped a finger on the map. "There is a similar steep, narrow portion of the trail here at Efogi. Is that not correct?"

"Yes, Admiral."

"Then would it not be logical to conduct air sorties that would close off the trail at Manari and Efogi?"

"You must forgive me if I disagree, Honorable Admiral," Lieutenant Sasai said. "If we destroy the trails at the points you suggest, we could hamper our own ground forces. We do, after all, expect the Honorable Horii to complete his march to Port Moresby. Would it be wise to destroy the trails at Manari and Efogi? General Horii can easily repair the bridges over the Mambare River with his excellent engineer companies, but he would need weeks to clear and repair the trails along the steep bluffs at Manari and Efogi."

Admiral Kasaka suddenly grinned. "I now understand why Captain Saito made you a squadron leader. And I must concede that you are in a better position to plan an assault on the enemy supply lines than I am. You have continually been conducting sorties over these Owen Stanley Mountains while I have never flown over these terrains. As long as you have the approval of your wing commander, Lieutenant, do whatever you think is best."

"Thank you, Honorable Admiral."

"Then all of us understand our parts in this endeavor?" Admiral Kasaka asked. When no one answered, the admiral continued. "Let us review. Two squadrons of the 4th Kokutai's A group, the heavy Mitsubishi bombers, will strike the enemy's lighter bomber and fighter plane runways at Moresby. Two squadrons of Mitsubishi fighter planes from the Tinian Wing will escort these heavy bombers. Next, the two squadrons of Aichi dive bombers from the 4th Kokutai's B Group will make sustained attacks on the enemy positions at Kokoda and they will be escorted by the Mitsubishi fighter squadrons from Salamaua. And finally, Lt. Junichi Sasai's Ten Squadron of the Tinian Wing will destroy the Mambare River bridges and the Myola Lake landing field. This squadron will further seek out and destroy any supplies and troop concentrations the enemy may have along the trail between Port Moresby and Kokoda. Is this not correct?"

Both Captain Shingo and Captain Saito nodded.

"I would ask again that these strikes be carried out simultaneously to give the enemy no chance to respond," Kasaka said. "I would also ask that these sorties be carried out at about 0830 hours tomorrow. Are there any objections?"

"No," Captain Shingo answered. "I shall have my bomber crews and squadron leaders ready their aircraft for strikes at 0830 hours."

"I have no objections," Captain Saito said. "Further, I will ask the squadron leaders of my wing to coordinate their time and place of rendezvous with the squadron leaders of the 4th Kokutai bomber squadrons."

"Very good," Admiral Kasaka said. "I'm sure, Captain, that you and Captain Shingo will carry out these strikes with your usual prowess and determination."

When the briefing ended, the 24th Air Flotilla commander flew immediately back to Rabaul. Then Capt. Masahisa Saito asked the squadron commanders of his Zero units at Salamaua to meet with Cmdr. Bunji Shimada on this same 10 August morning to coordinate their efforts for the strikes on Kokoda. Saito himself and his 11 Squadron leader, Lt. Cmdr. Tadashi Nakajima, met with Capt. Uehara Shingo and Lt. Toshio Handa, Shingo's 34 Squadron leader to arrange their coordination for the Port Moresby strikes. Shingo himself would lead his wing's A Group's 33 Squadron of Bettys while Lt. Toshio Handa led 34 Squadron.

Like so many others in the 24th Flotilla, both Lt. Cmdr. Tadashi Nakajima of the Tinian Wing and Lt. Toshio Handa of the 4th Kokutai were veterans in the Japanese naval air forces. Both men had served in China and Manchuria, and both had participated in the Japanese drives up the Malaysia Peninsula and into Indo China early in the war. Nakajima had been promoted to lieutenant commander in March of 1942. He had an excellent knack for spotting good pilots and when he did, he made every effort to get them into his squadron. While the 30 year old Nakajima often sympathized with pilots who suffered some unexpected difficulty, he would quickly dress down pilots who failed to carry out orders to the letter.

Lieutenant Handa was another quite young squadron commander, but a man who had shown remarkable leadership qualities early in his career. He had only joined the naval air forces in late 1940 and within a year he had risen in rank and won command of a Betty Bomber squadron. Despite his young age, Captain Shingo had great faith in Handa who had never disappointed the 4th Kokutai Wing commander.

Now the four Japanese air leaders completed their plans.

"Shall we rendezvous at the usual place?" Captain Saito asked. "At the Mambare River bend south of Wau?"

"We expect to leave Gasmata at 0630 hours and we should be at the rendezvous by 0800," Shingo said.

"Our escorts will be there," Saito said.

Shingo pursed his lips. "I know we have rarely seen enemy fighter planes north of the Mambare River bend. But with the raging ground war about Kokoda, is it possible that enemy interceptors could pounce on our bombers before we reach this expected rendezvous point? We expect to have about fifty heavy bombers from our 33 and 34 Squadrons."

Captain Saito shook his head. "We have seen no evidence of enemy fighter planes recently north of the bend, despite the battle at Kokoda. They still confine their sorties to escort duties for bombers that occasionally attack Lae or Salamaua. Or they make occasional attacks on our

47

ground troops near Kokoda. Even during the invasion of Buna, the enemy's fighter planes made few sweeps over the beaches. The enemy simply has too few of them and they must be used primarily to escort their even fewer bombers. Be assured, Captain Shingo, you will meet no enemy fighter planes before we rendezvous."

"The rendezvous must be precisely at 0800, with radio silence," Lieutenant Handa suddenly spoke, gesturing emphatically. "We must make this run into Port Moresby with the least possibility of detection."

"We understand," Captain Saito assured Lieutenant Handa.

Captain Shingo then spread a map on the table in front of him, a map that showed in detail the various Allied runways and dispersal areas at the sprawling base of Port Moresby. Japanese photo recon pilots had done a good job in studying Moresby.

"As you know, the enemy maintains several airdromes in Moresby," Shingo said, "but our interest is in three of them, the light bomber base, the American fighter runway, and the Australian base that maintains fighters and light bombers. We should destroy the Laloki Drome here that houses the American fighter plane units," Shingo placed a finger on the map. "If we destroy this runway, such fighter planes can no longer interfere with the efforts of the Nankai Shitai Detachment. We must also destroy the Australian air drome here, four miles inland from the Port Moresby port facilities. The Australian light bombers and fighter planes have been especially aggressive and annoying in supporting their ground forces at Kokoda. The Australian airmen are uncannily familiar with the terrain about Kokoda. Therefore, it is quite imperative that we eliminate their runway and as many of their aircraft as we can."

"And the third target is no doubt the runway at Koki," Captain Saito suddenly spoke.

"Yes, the runway at Koki, this one," Captain Shingo tapped a point on the map. "Above all, we should destroy Koki, the airdrome of the American light bomber group."

"The Yankee 3rd Bomb Sentai," Captain Saito said. "Of all the enemy units in Port Moresby, the light bombers and the B-25s of this unit have caused us the most distress. Their crews are courageous and brazen. They have many times mounted bombing raids against our fighter bases at Lae and Salamaua, sometimes even without escort. Despite heavy losses, they return again and again, and on occasions they have caused us serious damage. We of the Tinian Wing would feel sheer pleasure if you especially destroy this Koki runway."

"This same American air unit has made two air attacks on Buna, I am told by Commander Shimada," Lieutenant Handa said, "and they made these attacks despite the close proximity of our fighter planes at Salamaua. This 3rd Bomber Sentai would react quickly to our planned multiple strikes. They would even be foolish enough to attack Buna as they were the first to

49

attack our Buna landings; however they failed in the attempt."

Captain Shingo grinned at Lieutenant Handa. "We will use your entire 33 Squadron of heavy bombers to attack the Koki airdrome. Do you object?"

"You honor me with the request," Lieutenant Handa answered. "From what I have heard of this brazen American bomber unit, I will be delighted to destroy their base."

Captain Saito now looked at Lt. Cmdr. Tadashi Nakajima. "Commander, I would ask that you escort Lieutenant Handa's squadron."

Nakajima nodded.

"I assume, Captain," Saito now turned to the 4th Kokutai Wing commander, "that you will divide your other squadron to strike the Laloki Drome and the Australian air base."

"Yes," Shingo answered. "Our One and Two Flights of 33 Squadron will strike Laloki and our Three and Four Flights will strike the Australians."

"I will escort your One and Two Flights myself with the One and Two Flights of our 12 Squadron. The Three and Four Flights of 12 Squadron will escort those of your squadron who attack the Australian 4 Mile Drome."

"Excellent," Captain Shingo said. Then he snapped a finger and an aide immediately appeared before him with a tray of glasses and a saki bottle. When the aide laid the tray on the table, Shingo poured drinks and then passed the glasses to those about him. "A toast, honored men of the 24th Flotilla. Let us hope that our efforts tomorrow will assure victory in New Guinea."

"To a final victory in New Guinea," Capt. Masahisa Saito answered.

Then the wing and squadron leaders about the table raised their glasses and downed their saki.

CHAPTER THREE

The air commanders of Tinian and 4th Kokutai Wings had ample reason to single out the 3rd Bomb Group as a particularly annoying air unit. Since the Japanese first landed in northern Papua in March to occupy Lae and Salamaua, the American 3rd Group, the Grim Reapers, had continually harassed them, despite the superiority of the 24th Air Flotilla.

Since the 3rd Bomb Group went into combat in March, the Grim Reapers had taken a heavy toll against the Japanese. No sooner had the Japanese established their air base in Lae when, on 1 April, the 3rd struck the base with A-20s, knocking out five planes and punching holes in the newly completed airstrip. The 3rd then continued hitting both Lae and Salamaua at every opportunity with their A-24 and A-20 light bombers and their B-25 medium bombers. These raids often cost the 3rd heavy losses and did not badly hurt the Japanese, but they caused considerable damage to runways and dispersal areas, necessitating constant repair and the need for constant replacement of planes and equipment. The losses had irritated the Japanese who were unaccustomed to losing anything much during the near total success in the Pacific War since Pearl Harbor.

The 3rd had been the first unit to strike the Japanese after the Nankai Shitai Detachment invaded Buna on 21 July, and the Grim Reapers had caused the most damage to supplies stacked on the Buna beaches. The 3rd, along with Australian aircraft, had made frequent strikes against Japanese troops and Japanese supply lines as the Yokoyama Force moved inland from Buna to Kokoda. Gen. Tomitaro Horii, the Nankai Shitai commander, had more than once cursed the American 3rd Sentai while he pressed the Tinian Wing to destroy this pesky American air unit.

"How can you allow these brazen Yankee airmen to strike our troop concentrations and supply dumps so often with such immunity," Horii once scolded Captain Saito. In fact, the annoyance from the 3rd Bomb Group strikes against the Japanese in the Kokoda area had been the principal factor in General Horii's request for the massive air strikes against the Port Moresby runways.

While the efforts of the 3rd Group did not stop the Japanese, the air attacks by the Grim Reapers constantly reminded the Japanese that somebody on the other side was fighting back.

Whatever success the 3rd Group had enjoyed in New Guinea against overwhelming Japanese air superiority could probably be traced to Col. John Davies, the Grim Reaper commander.

Davies, slender, tall, and with a classic square face, had been in the Pacific since the beginning of hostilities in December of 1941. In the Philippines, he had commanded the 27th Bomb Group, a medium B-25 unit based at Del Monte on the island of Mindanao. From this field, Davies had fought against untold odds and he had seen his B-25s fall one by one. By the time he retreated to Java, only a dozen B-25s remained. After operating out of Java for several weeks, he had become the commander of a mere ghost unit. His 27th Bomb Group had no more planes and Davies with his 27th survivors evacuated to Darwin, Australia.

In March of 1942 General Brett had asked Davies to assume command of the recently arrived 3rd Bomb Group that had been in existence since World War I, beginning as the 104th Aero Squadron. When Davies reached Chartres Towers in northeast Australia, he found a mixture of flying crews. Some had been experienced flyers who had survived the Philippine and Java campaigns; others were raw crews just over from the states. He found a mixed bag of aircraft: 33 A-24s, 20 A-20 light bombers, and a dozen B-25s. Davies assigned the A-20s to 89th Squadron, the B-25s to the 13th Squadron, and the A-24s to the 8th and 90th Squadrons. He had scattered his experienced crews from the old 27th Group among the four squadrons so that all squadrons had a share of combat experienced men.

Between March and July of 1942, the air war over New Guinea had taken a toll. The 3rd Group had lost most of its B-25s, most of its A-24s, and half of its A-20s. Promised replacements had only included about a dozen A-20s and about a dozen repaired B-25s and A-24s.

At the time the Japanese air leaders had completed their briefings at Buna on 10 August 1942, Davies had 34 aircraft in the 3rd Group: ten A-24 single engine light bombers, the army version of the U. S. Navy's Dauntless; ten B-25s, the twin engine medium bomber; and fourteen A-20s, the twin engine light bomber.

The 10 August air meeting at Buna did not go unnoticed by the new 5th Air Force. PBY four engine bombers and speedy, lightly armed P-40s made continual reconnaisance flights to keep the Allies informed of Japanese activities. The Allies enjoyed the added advantage of Papuan native scouts, who reported regularly to ANGAU authorities on Japanese movements. At noon, 10 August 1942, Colonel Davies and one of his squadron commanders, Maj. Bob Strickland of the 3rd Group's 89th Squadron, were in the 3rd Group headquarters at Koki Drome. They were discussing plans for their next air strike when an aide brought Davies a report.

After Davies read the report, he frowned.

"What's up?" Strickland asked.

Davies tossed the report to Strickland. "The

Japanese are up to something."

"They're always up to something," Strickland scowled.

"Something big this time," Davies said. "According to these air recon reports, and reports from Papuan scouts, a lot of high air brass met in Buna this morning. They think one of the planes that came to Buna was the converted Betty bomber aircraft of the Japanese air commander himself. They also think that all the wing and squadron commanders of the 24th Air Flotilla were there."

"What the hell can they can be up to?" the major wondered.

"I don't know," Davies said. "Maybe they're planning an all out air assault on Kokoda so they can drive the Australians out of there once and for all. Maybe they're planning to hit Moresby again, much harder this time."

"They're always hitting Moresby," Strickland scoffed.

"I'm going to see Whitehead right after noon mess to find out if he knows anything more. Meanwhile, keep our planes on the ready; we may go out ourselves this afternoon to hit those Nip troops around Kokoda again."

"Okay, Johnny," Maj. Bob Strickland answered.

At 1300 hours, John Davies drove to the rickety Port Moresby Hotel, the headquarters for the advanced operational echelon of 5th Air Force. Gen. Ennis Whitehead, the 5th Air Force ADVON commander, was still eating his noonday meal when Davies arrived. Nonetheless, he asked Davies to come right into his office. When Davies came inside, he noted Whitehead eating the same dehydrated potatoes, bully beef, and half slice of canned peaches that every American airman in Port Moresby had eaten for lunch today. And Whitehead was clad in his battered shirt and his usual battered shorts, cut from a pair of old khaki trousers. Only the gold star of a brigadier general on the collar of his open shirt distinguished Whitehead from the lowliest airman in Port Moresby.

"Sit down, Johnny," Whitehead gestured before he took another mouthful of his spuds and bully beef.

"How the hell can you eat that stuff with such relish," John Davies grinned.

"When you're hungry, anything tastes good," Whitehead answered.

Brig. Gen. Ennis Whitehead was a big man, tall and muscular, and a former football player at West Point. His hefty weight was evenly distributed about his body. Despite his 47 years, Whitehead exercised regularly and he no doubt needed plenty of nourishment to maintain his bully frame.

Gen. George Kenney, when he took command of 5th Air Force, had appointed Whitehead the 5th Air Force ADVON commander. While Kenney was an excellent administrative specialist, he lacked any World War II combat experience. so he wanted a man with such experience as his operational commander.

The man Kenney designated, Ennis White-head, had been a fighter pilot in both World War I and World War II, and a man who willingly shared the discomforts of combat crews under him. Whitehead was a down to earth air leader who frowned on luxury or formalities. While he did set up his headquarters in the hotel, his own personal quarters was a steaming canvas tent that was no better than the accommodations of the lowest airman.

The huge and burly Whitehead had a big, rough face with a dented nose. His gravel voice rang with the same authority as a loading dock boss, a ring that projected an image of strength and durability among his men. In his tattered attire he looked like a yardbird private. Only upon close inspection, when the brigadier star on his shirt collar became clear, did a man know that this rugged individual was a general.

When Whitehead took over ADVON he quickly eliminated all confusion with a simple directive: "Any man who fails to follow my instructions will be immediately relieved of duty and court martialed." Whitehead had told his staff: "This is war and I expect every man to work twenty hours a day, seven days a week. I can do it and so can every airman in this command."

The 5th Air Force airmen, unaccustomed to such brash, authoritative warnings, felt uneasy about Whitehead. They were not sure they liked him, but they suspected they had better obey him. The airmen quickly tabbed Whitehead the "Old Man," since, at age 47, Whitehead was much older than the 20 or even 30 year olds in 5th Air Force. Davies himself was 28.

On this early afternoon of 10 August, the gruff 5th Air Force ADVON commander swallowed the last of his jungle fare lunch. "Well, Johnny?"

"Those recon and scouting reports on Buna," Davies said. "Are the Japanese up to something big?"

"How the hell do I know," Whitehead answered. "But I don't like the reports of all that air brass in Buna."

"Maybe we can hit Buna this afternoon to break up whatever they might have in mind."

"You know better than that," Whitehead said. "All we can do is react to their initiatives. We just don't have the punch to do anything more. We can only try to contain the bastards until Washington gets off its ass and sends us enough planes and crews to punch back."

"They might shove us into the Coral Sea by then," Davies said.

"Jesus, Johnny, you've lost enough men and planes. The cost has just been too goddamn high. Every time you go out, I'm afraid you won't come back. If I send you out this afternoon, you'll just lose more planes and men because I don't think Buzz Wagner can get a squadron of P-40s out this afternoon."

"Then we just do nothing?"

Whitehead reached to a corner of his desk, flipped through some papers, and pulled a sheet from the stack. "The Aussies up at Kokoda are screaming for air support. They say the Japanese are massing again to hit them once more. General Morris isn't sure his boys up in those mountains can stop the bastards this time. I'm going to meet with my staff in a half hour and then we'll meet with General Morris to find out how he wants a new support mission for Kokoda. Right now, Kokoda is our first priority and we can't worry about what the Japanese are planning at Buna. Your A-20s and A-24s will go along with the Beauforts of the Aussie 22 Squadron. I'll ask the 35th Group and the Australian 75 Squadron to ready some P-39s and P-40s to give you escort cover. Maybe we can send out forty or fifty planes and do some real damage to those Japanese crawling around Kokoda."

"Okay, Ennis," John Davies said.

The 3rd Bomb Group commander felt a mixture of disappointment and relief as he drove back to Koki Airdrome. Davies had an obsession to hit the Japanese whenever he could, but he also knew that Whitehead was right. If he went out today to hit Buna, especially without escorts from Buzz Wagner's 8th Fighter Group, he could lose a lot of his aircraft to the Japanese Zeros.

The morning of 11 August 1942 broke relatively clear with only scattered puffs of clouds drifting over the usually moisture-laden skies of Papua in eastern New Guinea. Today was a good day for an air strike.

At the Allied base in Port Moresby, word from 5th Air Force ADVON headquarters had reached the 3rd Bomb Group, the 35th Fighter Group, the RAAF 22 Squadron and the RAAF 75 Squadron: prepare for late morning strikes in the Kokoda area. Estimated time over targets would be at 1030 hours; take off time from Port Moresby about 1000 hours for the short eighty mile flight to Kokoda in the middle of the Owen Stanleys. By 0800 hours, ground mechanics leisurely serviced aircraft, and ordnance men loaded bombs and boxes of .50 caliber strafing belts on dolly trailers before dragging the trailers with small tractors to arm the aircraft in their dispersal areas. Col. John Davies and other group commanders had posted briefing times for 0900 hours for the mid-morning strikes.

At the same 0800 hours, 47 Betty bombers of the Kokutai Wing's A Group had already been airborne for an hour and a half, all the way from Gasmata on the south coast of New Britain. Capt. Uehara Shingo, from the cabin of his lead Betty bomber looked at the Bettys on either side of him in the first V. Soon, he saw the bend in the Mambare River—rendezvous point. As Shingo searched the skies about him, they were empty. He panicked for a moment. But then, he saw the dots in the distance at two o'clock—the Zero escorts from Lae. Captain Shingo relaxed. Almost instinctively, the 4th Kokutai commander went for his radio mike, but his arm stopped abruptly. No, he must maintain radio silence, and the thought sent a slight tremor through his body. Suppose a mix-up occurred with the Zero escorts? Suppose they missed their proper positions?

But Captain Masahisa Saito of the Tinian Fighter Wing made no mistakes. He had briefed well the pilots of his 11 and 12 Squadrons. Almost like synchronized aerial acrobats, the Zero pilots brought their aircraft next to their bomber charges. Lt. Cmdr. Tadashi Nakajima took the Mitsubishis of his 11 Squadron and formed a ring around the trailing 34 Squadron of Bettys that would hit the Port Moresby Koki Airdrome, home of the pesky U. S. 3rd Bomb Group. Capt. Masahisa Saito himself closed around the first two flights of 33 Squadron Bettys with the first two flights of his own 12 Squadron Zeros. The other flights of 12 Squadron closed around the 3 and 4 Flights of 33 Squadron.

When the Zeros had settled next to the Bettys, the array of Japanese planes fell in unison to hug the tall peaks of the Owen Stanleys. They would fly as low as possible for as long as possible to avoid detection.

Captain Shingo's only concern now was Moresby itself. He hoped that each of his bomber crews struck the correct target when they unleashed their 500 pound bombs. Shingo looked at the nearly clear skies above him and he was satisfied. He would have good visual for the run over targets and he should enjoy maximum accuracy.

For another half hour, the 47 bombers and their 54 Zero escorts skimmed the high, lofty peaks of the Owen Stanley Mountains. Then as the droning planes reached Imita Ridge, Captain Shingo pulled back the wheel of his G-M 4 bomber and the Betty rose upward. Shingo watched the altimeter needle rise to 10,000 feet and then he leveled off. When he looked about him, he saw that the other planes of his 33 and 34 Squadrons had also leveled off at 10,000 feet, with the Tinian Wing Zeros still clinging alongside them.

At 0825 hours, the air raid sirens suddenly wailed across Port Moresby from a half dozen different areas. Red alert! Men scrambled from buildings, grass huts, tents, runways, or dispersal areas to hurry into foxholes. Several Aussie pilots of 75 Squadron and a dozen P-39 pilots of the 8th Fighter Group ran to their Kittyhawks and Air-acobras, hoping to take off and intercept the enemy planes. But they would not get off the ground before the first whistling bombs fell on Moresby. In fact, they would barely abandon their planes and reach foxholes before the first explosions rocked their airdromes.

The Japanese had followed their usual pattern of coming low all across the Owen Stanleys before climbing to bombing altitude over Imita Ridge, some 30 miles from Moresby. Thus, before interceptors got off the ground, the Bettys would already begin their bomb runs.

At exactly 0830, the 500 pound explosives from each Betty aircraft sailed downward from the bomb bays of 23 G-M 4 bombers in Lt. Toshio Handa's 34 Squadron. Every Betty pilot from the squadron had aimed his bombs on the 3rd Group's Koki Airdrome. Fortunately for the Grim Reapers, the pilots of the Japanese Bettys struck with their usual poor aim. At least half the bombs from 34 Squadron went awry, gouging huge chunks out of surrounding kunai plains or blasting away jungle trees in the dense forest areas around Koki.

Other 500 pound explosives directly or nearly directly struck two A-24s, one A-20, and a B-25 in the 3rd Group revetment areas. The thunderous explosions destroyed the four aircraft. The two A-24s blew apart in fiery balls of shrapnel. The A-20 bounced off the ground and exploded before coming down in a heap of tangled, twisted metal. The B-25 caught a shattering explosion directly on its nose and the blast disintegrated the forward section of the plane, leaving the aircraft like a two tailed, headless whale.

The more damaging aspect of Koki drome, however, was the attack on the runway. Nearly forty 500 pound bombs fell on the airstrip, chopping out huge chunks of earth in a staccato of numbing explosions that spewed dirt and shrapnel dozens of feet into the air. By the time the smoke and dust cleared, the Koki runway resembled a totally potholed stretch of highway. Some of the holes measured 30 feet across and fifteen to 20 feet deep.

Meanwhile, Capt. Uehara Shingo split his 33 Squadron, with 12 Bettys striking 12 Mile Drome, home of the 8th and 35th U.S. Fighter Groups. Another 12 Bettys hit 4 Mile Drome that housed the P-40s and Beauforts of the Australian 9th RAAF Group's 75 and 22 Squadrons. Once more, however, the aim of the Betty bomber pilots was not totally accurate, especially when heavy 40mm and 37mm anti-aircraft fire challenged the Japanese interlopers. Heavy, exploding puffs of ack-ack fire sent two of the Bettys down in flames, damaged several more of the G-M 4 aircraft, and spoiled the aim of other pilots.

Still, the Japanese caused extensive damage to both 12 Mile and 4 Mile Dromes. Exploding 500 pounders tore apart four P-39s of Col. Buzz Wagner's 8th Fighter Group and two P-39s of the U.S. 35th Fighter Group. The small American fighter planes literally blew apart from the numbing explosions. Further, more than twenty 500 pounders fell on the 12 Mile drome runway, deeply potting the length of the runway and leaving large pits and mounds of dirt. When the smoke and dust cleared, the airstrip looked like a highway construction site in its initial stages.

More 500 pound bombs from the Japanese 33 Squadron whistled into the Australian RAAF 9th Group 4 Mile Drome. Two of the 22 Squadron's Beauforts caught direct hits and erupted in balls of fire before balls of smoke enveloped the aircraft. More G-M 4 explosives knocked out three Kittyhawks of the Australian 75 Squadron, tearing the P-40s asunder as other 500 pounders had torn apart the six Airacobras of the American fighter groups at 12 Mile Drome. Another dozen or more 500 pounders ripped into the runway and left huge holes on the 4 Mile Airdrome airstrip.

Then, for good measure, some of the Betty bombers attacked a half dozen parked C-47 transport planes that had been supplying the

Australians at Kokada by air. Exploding bombs wrecked two of the C-47s and damaged two more.

As the bombers finished their runs and turned northward, the Zero fighter planes of Tinian Wing came low to rake the same three airdromes at Port Moresby with rattling .30 caliber machine gun fire and whooshing 20mm cannon fire. The Zeros enjoyed little success, however, because of heavy anti-aircraft fire from the 40mm and 37mm guns that quickly knocked down three of the low flying Mitsubishi fighter planes and damaged three more of the Japanese fighters. Still, the Zero attack destroyed the other two C-47 transport planes and also destroyed three more combat planes.

When the Japanese aerial assault ended, and the Bettys and Zeros had disappeared over the Owen Stanleys, the Australian and American airmen at Port Moresby came out of their shelters and stared in awe at the crackling fires and palls of oily smoke around their runways.

Big John Davies ambled toward the Koki airstrip with Maj. Bob Strickland and several other 3rd Group officers trailing after him. "The dirty bastards," the Grim Reaper commander cursed. "They worked us over good this time."

"When are we going to hit back, Colonel? When?" one of the pilots asked angrily.

"How do I know," Davies answered gruffly.

"Christ, it'll take a week before they repair this runway; at least a week," another pilot moaned.

"What the hell do you want me to do about it?"

Davies asked. He moved briskly away from the others, but stopped abruptly when a crew chief came toward him. "Well, Sergeant? How much damage?"

"Not too bad, sir," the sergeant said. "They're still crosseyed when it comes to accuracy. With all those planes they could have leveled us from the bay all the way to Imita Ridge. We got maybe six planes out of commission; no more. I think we can put two of them back in shape pretty quick."

"Don't rush," Davies scowled. "We're grounded for at least a few days."

At the other two Port Moresby dromes, the airmen felt equally rattled. Col. Boyd Buzz Wagner of the 8th Fighter Group and Capt. Tom Lynch of the 35th Fighter Group surveyed the damage about their smoldering 12 Mile Drome along the Laloki River. The two American fighter pilots had lost about a half dozen P-39s between the two groups from the Japanese aerial assaults. But they were more dismayed by the damage to their runway.

"Goddamn, Colonel," Capt. Tom Lynch huffed, "they never tore us up this bad before. They wanted our runways; just the runways of our fighter planes and light bombers. They never went near the heavy strip at 7 Mile Drome."

"The bastards," Wagner cursed. "They don't want any of our support planes off today. The sons 'a bitches don't want any of our planes around Kokoda for a while. They want to take the mesa and they can do it a lot easier if they don't have to worry about air support from us, from the 3rd Bomb Group, and from the Aussie air units."

Buzz Wagner, like John Davies, had been in the Pacific since the outbreak of war in 1941. The tall, handsome fighter pilot from Pittsburgh Pa. had been a fighter pilot with the old 24th Pursuit Squadron at Clark Field in the Philippines. He had gained his nickname Buzz from an almost uncontrollable habit of buzzing other planes in the air, a sometimes dangerous maneuver. Still, perhaps no man in the U.S. Air Force knew a P-39 better than the 8th Group colonel. He had shot down seven enemy planes in the Philippines, often against tremendous odds.

In late December Wagner caught pieces of glass in his eye when his cockpit was struck by strafing fire in aerial combat. He had been evacuated to Australia where doctors removed the glass fragments and said he would probably never fly again. But Wagner recovered and assumed command of the newly arrived 8th Fighter Group that included 60 new P-39s. After two months of fighting in New Guinea, the group had lost half of its planes and pilots.

Now Wagner felt another sense of frustration, in this continually losing air war against the Japanese. He turned again to Captain Lynch. "Those poor Diggers at Kokoda. Without air support, they'll really catch hell now."

"Yeh," Tom Lynch nodded. The 35th group squadron leader could say nothing else.

At the smoking 4 Mile Drome, the squadron leaders of 22 and 75 Squadrons surveyed the damage to their runway and aircraft with the same angry frustration. Air Cmdr. Frank Lukis of 22 Squadron had lost two of his Beaufort light bombers to the Japanese Bettys. Lt. Larry Jackson, leader of 75 Squadron, had lost three P-40s destroyed and three more damaged. But like the American air commanders, these Aussie air leaders also bemoaned the heavy destruction to their runway that might keep them grounded for several days, plenty of time for the Japanese Nankai Shitai Detachment to work over the Australian infantry troops at Kokoda without Allied air interference.

"Our poor blokes in those mountains," Lieutenant Jackson shook his head, "they'll 'ave an 'ard time, they will, without air support—such as it is. If those bloody Nips 'it them as 'ard as the Nips 'it us this morning, those Diggers won't 'ave a chance."

"The Nips knew what they were after," A/C Frank Lukis said.

"We 'aven't lost too many planes, Frank," Jackson said. "Can we use one of the other airdromes?"

" 'Ow the 'ell can we taxi Beauforts and Kittyhawks over this goddamn kunai grass? Anyway, from what I 'ear, the only strip they missed was the 'eavy bomb 7 Mile Drome at Waigani."

"Maybe we can fly in some Kittyhawks from Milne Bay to 7 Mile," Jackson said.

"Maybe," Lukis answered. But there was little enthusiasm in his voice.

From the warped, weatherbeaten porch of the

old Port Moresby Hotel, Gen. Ennis Whitehead stared at the fire and smoke that crackled and drifted over three of his Port Moresby airdromes. Whitehead wore a deep scowl on his face, leaving an even more grotesque look on his bent nosed countenance.

"Son of a bitch! Son of a bitch!" Only this repeated malediction came from the general's deep gravel voice.

Two 5th Air Force ADVON aides stood behind the general, but neither man spoke while Whitehead unwound. Not until the ADVON commander finally stopped cursing and heaved a sigh, did one of the aides step forward.

"7 Mile hasn't been touched, sir," the aide said. "Should we get the 22nd and 43rd Groups up here with their B-26s and B-17s? Maybe they can hit back in the morning."

"You're crazy, Captain," Whitehead answered. "You think I'm going to send out Marauders and Fortresses without fighter escort? With the skies to the north swarming with Zeros? No," he shook his head vigorously. "We're simply out of business until we get these runways repaired. Let's just hope the Japanese are content with their handiwork here in Moresby this morning."

But the Japanese were hardly content with their shattering 11 August raid on Port Moresby, the 78th raid on this major Allied base since the Japanese occupied Lae and Salamaua in March of 1942.

CHAPTER FOUR

At the same 0830 hours that Captain Shingo's Betty bombers were dropping 500 pounders on Port Moresby, Val dive bombers approached the Kokoda area. Cmdr. Bunji Shimada was leading the B Group's 35 Squadron planes of the 4th Kokutai Wing toward the mountain high target. While the Japanese had struck Kokoda several times since the landings in Buna, they had never roared over the mesa with so many planes.

Shimada saw only clear skies ahead and no sign of enemy interceptors to forestall his dive bombing attacks. He knew that Japanese infantry troops of the Nankai Shitai Detachment were just behind the mesa and ready to close in as soon as the 4th Wing's bombers completed their work. Shimada had come within five minutes of Kokoda when the commander saw the formations off to the west—30 Zero fighters from the Tinian Wing's 15 Squadron out of Salamaua. Shimada grinned, widening his round face. His escort was on time.

At exactly 0837 hours, within five miles of the Kokoda mesa, Commander Shimada broke radio silence to seek his coordinates for the bomb runs. He called the Nankai Shitai signal platoon just south of Kokoda, where Gen. Tomitaro Horii himself answered the 35 Squadron commander.

"Commander," Horii said, "we have carefully reconnoitered the enemy defenses at Kokoda and we have carefully noted the Australian's strongest positions. Please refer to your map and mark these coordinates: .032, .037, and .039. We would like you to attack at those points."

"Yes, Honorable Horii," Shimada answered.

"We have also prepared a mortar and artillery barrage for the Australian dogs," Horii continued. "As soon as you have completed your bombardment and strafing runs over the Kokoda mesa, we shall commence firing."

"We shall attack at exactly 0840 hours," Shimada said. "But there are more dive bombers coming after us. 36 Squadron will attack at 0930 hours and our own 35 Squadron will return at 1030 hours."

"Good," General Horii said. "We will lacerate the Australians with mortar and artillery in between your air strikes."

Moments later, Commander Shimada cried into his radio. "All pilots will attack in pairs; in pairs." Then: "Banzai!"

Commander Shimada gestured to his wingman and then banked right before he and his wingman droned above the jungle trees at about 1000 feet and roared toward the Kokoda target. The Australians cowered in their foxholes as the first bombs sailed into their defenses, exploding in deafening barks. Another pair of Vals also unleashed four bombs over the area that also shattered the thick jungle brakes. Snapping branches crackled and thudded to the damp jungle floor. Leaves flew about like huge green snowflakes. The stench of misty powder radiated through the jungle.

For ten minutes the Aussie Diggers huddled tensely in their holes while exploding bombs shook the terrain and shattered trees. Fortunately, most of the bursting shrapnel had exploded short and caused little damage. Unfortunately, the last flight of Vals scored hits on foxholes, blowing away the lives of six Diggers and opening deep shrapnel wounds in a dozen more. Within these unlucky foxholes, blood flowed in torrents, mixing with the soft mud and forming a macabre wad of mushy, reddish mire. Several of the Papuan native troops also died from direct hits or near direct hits on their shelters.

When the Japanese 35 Squadron dropped its last bombs, the Vals banked wide and returned in low, treetop level sweeps, unleashing strafing and 20mm cannon fire. Once more, leaves scattered off trees, brush flew upward and pops of soil rose from the damp jungle floor. A few more Aussies were wounded and three more Diggers were killed.

While the Australians at Kokoda staggered about their positions in numb horror, they got no respite. A sudden barrage of mortar and 37mm mountain artillery pummelled into Kokoda to cause more suffering and more destruction to equipment and supplies. When the barrage ended, the Australian Diggers at Kokoda were totally lacerated and exhausted.

But still the Japanese were not finished. At 0930 came another swarm of Val dive bombers to pummel the Australians again with hundred pound fragmentation and incendiary bombs, four bombs skimming into the Australian positions from each Aichi 99 aircraft. And when these planes were gone, a new barrage of artillery and mortar from Horii's jungle hidden positions again slammed into the Australians. Once more men died, men bled, and supplies went up in fire and smoke.

The Australians at Kokoda desperately called Port Moresby for air support to stop the Val dive bombing assaults and jungle artillery attacks. But the Diggers were stunned when they learned that Japanese Bettys had pulverized the Moresby runways and that no planes could come to their aid.

While screaming 37mm artillery shells and 30mm mortar shells exploded on the Australian perimeters, Cmdr. Bunji Shimada led his 35 Squadron Vals once more over the same Kokoda targets at 1030 hours. The swooping Aichi 99s ripped up Digger defenses with more screaming 100 pound bombs, chattering 7.7 machine gun fire, and 20mm cannon shells. In moments, the entire 300 yard L of trenches became a smoking, burning holocaust. More than 50 Diggers died, their bodies torn apart by exploding shrapnel, bursting bombs, or penetrating 7.7 machine gun fire.

Still General Horii made no attempt to mount a frontal assault on the decimated Australians. Why should he? As long as his air units could strike the enemy at Kokoda without fear of interception by enemy fighters, and as long as enemy bombers could not make strikes of their own or hit Horii's jungle positions, he need only have patience. Horii would wait until dark, surround the Australians and close in on what was left of them in the morning.

Further, Horii got added good news on this morning of 11 August. Lt. Junichi Sasai of the Tinian Wing's 10 Squadron had made his runs over the Australian supply lines on this devastating day for the Allies. Using his Zeros as fighter-bombers, Sasai met no opposition as he and his pilots successfully destroyed the bamboo bridges over the Mambare River, while other aircraft of his squadron chopped apart the small landing strip on the dry Myola Lake bed. Further, his 10 Squadron had also destroyed two Australian supply dumps on the Kokoda Trail between Moresby and Kokoda. Days would pass before native carriers or even the smallest planes could bring new supplies to the beleaguered Australian

Diggers at Kokoda.

By the late morning of 11 August, the advantage lay totally with the Japanese. Their superior air units had fully worked over the Allied airstrips at Moresby, the Aussie defenders at Kokoda, and the Australian supply lines. Now, some 5,000 jungle troops of the Nankai Shitai Detachment could continue their drive without Allied air interference. How could these Aussie Diggers, reduced to a thousand men, even with their reinforcements, stop such a drive?

By the evening of 11 August, General Horii's troops had surrounded the Kokoda mesa for their pincer in the morning. However the Australians fully recognized the tactic and they knew they were spent and without help. They would be annihilated in the morning. So during the night of 11-12 August, they quietly evacuated the Kokoda mesa, taking their wounded with them, but leaving their dead behind as well as most of the equipment and supplies. Horii was disappointed when he moved into Kokoda on the morning of 12 August and found the Australians gone.

"Bakarya (Bastards)!" the Japanese Nankai Shitai commander cursed.

Horii had hoped to wipe out the Australian survivors in the morning. Instead, the Diggers had slipped away. Irate, he turned to an aide. "We will move at once to Deniki to join Colonel Yokoyama's advance force and encircle the Australians again. Tomorrow we shall destroy them."

"Yes, Honorable Horii," his aide said.

General Horii now took full advantage of his

superior position. By mid-morning of 12 August he worked his troops into a frenzy and then started swiftly after the retreating Diggers. A fresh Australian battalion, about 800 men, arrived to join the Diggers who had escaped from Kokoda. But they would not be enough to stop the thousands of Japanese troops.

And worse, over the past few weeks, tons of food, supplies and heavy arms had reached the Japanese general's new headquarters at Isurava. Horii now struck viciously at the next Australian defense line at Templeton's Crossing, with a tidal wave of artillery, infantry troops, and air attacks. The Australians fell back, withdrawing down the precarious Kokoda Trail.

While the Americans worked frantically to repair their Moresby airstrips, Japanese Vals from Commander Shimada's B group at Buna and Japanese Zeros from Captain Saito's Tinian Wing at Lae continually pounded the retreating Australians. Further, both the Bettys and Vals hit Moresby again to chop up almost completely repaired runways.

Horii, sensing the kill, gave the Australians no rest. All during the latter part of August and into September, the Japanese chased the Australians from one patch of jungle to another, across one kunai field to the next, down one succeeding length of the Kokoda Trail to another, and from one village to the next: Efogi, Kagi, Manari. By the first week of September, the Australians had retreated to the jungles north of Ioribaiwa, with the Japanese on their heels.

"Our men need rest," Colonel Yokoyama told General Horii. "We have made rapid progress over many miles of hostile terrain under extreme conditions."

"We shall not stop as long as the road to Port Moresby remains open," General Horii answered. "We have the Australians in full retreat and the Honorable Kasaka's air squadrons have effectively thwarted the allied air units."

But, Horii's own troops had begun to weaken in the harsh jungle south of Templeton's Crossing. The swift advance through the Owen Stanleys had taken a logistical toll on the Japanese. Horii's soldiers had moved too fast for supplies to catch up to them. The combat troops of the Nakai Shitai Detachment were down to their last bags of rice. They were without medicine and they had dangerously depleted their ammunition. But still Horii pushed his troops on for several more days. On 8 September, Horii made his first attack on the Australians at Ioribaiwa, but the Australians held. However, the end was inevitable and after continued Japanese onslaughts, the Australians were forced to retreat once more.

At 1130 hours, 9 September, General Morris's Digger troops abandoned Ioribaiwa and fell back to Imita Ridge, five miles south. The Japanese were now 32 miles from Port Moresby. Horii was anxious to continue the pursuit, but if his troops did not rest and await supplies, the soldiers might drop from sheer exhaustion. They would find themselves eating roots and tree bark to survive.

Col. Yosuke Yokoyama pleaded with Horii.

"It is futile to continue on with our troops so weak. We must first ask our air units to destroy the Australian defenses at Imita. And we must await new supplies, perhaps in two or three weeks. By then, our men will have regained their strength. Then we can confidently continue our drive to Port Moresby."

"I must concede that you are right," General Horii finally admitted. "We will first rest here, await new supplies, and then continue our mission. Meanwhile, we will construct strong positions here in the event the Australians foolishly attempt a counter attack."

In truth, never was the Allied position more critical than this second week of September in 1942. The Allied air units had taken a battering since the enemy's drive from Kokoda—those that could get airborne. Most of the 5th Air Force units had been grounded much of the time from the Betty air strikes on runways, although newly arrived heavy equipment enabled engineers to repair runways more rapidly. But the Allied air crews were depressed and Australian ground troops were equally demoralized. Only one battalion of the Australian 7th Division was in Port Moresby and the three battalions from the Australian 30 Brigade were badly riddled and spent from the gruelling Owen Stanleys fight. The 39 Battalion of the 30th was totally unfit for combat.

And the worst was yet to come.

On 12 September, three days after the Japanese Nankai Shitai Detachment had captured Ioribaiwa, only 32 miles from Moresby, a patrolling 5th Air Force PBY spotted a Japanese surface ship convoy in the Solomon Sea, about a hundred miles from Buna. The convoy included five maru freighters under escort by four destroyers. No doubt, these vessels carried new supplies for the Japanese forces now in Buna and Kokoda and for the Yazawa Force of the Nankai Shitai Detachment that was expected to arrive soon. The pilot of the PBY reconnaissance plane guessed that the convoy was less than a day out of Buna. He quickly called 5th Air Force ADVON at Moresby. ADVON, in return, requested both the 3rd Bomb Group and the Australian 22 Squadron to launch an attack on the approaching Japanese convoy.

Since the 11 August air attacks, a host of new 'cats and bulldozers had arrived at Moresby to speed the repair of runways. So by the morning of 12 September, 5th Air Force engineers had runways in operating condition.

At 0800, on 12 September, Col. John Davies sat at the end of the runway of 3 Mile Airdrome in Port Moresby, the Koki Airdrome. The two engines of his B-25 whined furiously and the plane rocked like an anxious thoroughbred. In the bomb bay, Davies carried four 500 pound bombs. Behind his cabin, in the top turret, Gunner Elbert Jones scanned the blue skies above and then fingered the triggers of his .50 caliber guns. Jones had plenty of faith in Colonel Davies, but the B-

25 gunner was not certain he could do much with his two guns if they ran into a swarm of Zeros. When the green control light blinked, Colonel Davies roared down the runway and soared skyward. Jones looked behind him and watched the other five B-25s of the 13th Squadron turn from the taxi strip and onto the runway before they too roared down the runway and took off.

Next came six A-24s from the 3rd Group's 89th Squadron under Maj. Bob Strickland. The six Dauntlesses soon followed the B-25s into the New Guinea sky.

Then 12 light Beaufort bombers from the Australian 22 Squadron roared off 4 Mile Drome to follow the American 3rd Group.

A half hour later, sixteen P-39s of the 35th American Fighter Group's 39th Squadron under Capt. Tom Lynch roared down 12 Mile Airdrome's airstrip. Thomas Lynch had been a fighter pilot in the Philippines with the 18th Pursuit Squadron, and he had escaped from Luzon with the bulk of the squadron in January of 1942. He had joined the 35th Fighter Group in the Java campaign where he became the squadron commander of the group's 39th Squadron.

On 26 May, Lynch had downed two Japanese planes over Moresby, the very day the 35th had moved to Moresby to relieve the battered Australian 16 Squadron. The kills, numbers five and six, had made Lynch an ace. Lynch, besides tangling with Zero interceptors on many occasions, had also led his squadron on occasional fighter-bomber sorties. However, Lynch and his 39th

Squadron pilots carried no bombs today, for their mission was strictly to escort the 3rd Bomb Group against any Zero interceptors.

The P-39s would catch up to the B-25s and A-24s just before the bombers reached Buna where they would hover at 10 to 12 thousand feet to fend off any Japanese fighter planes that might interfere with the 3rd Group attack on the convoy. Still, Capt. Tom Lynch hoped they met no Zeros over Buna, for invariably, they always lost aircraft in dogfights against the higher numbers of Zeros that were superior to his P-39s in maneuverability, climb, and dive.

Finally, at 0845 hours, 12 P-40s from the Aussie 75 Squadron left 12 Mile Drome to escort a dozen Beauforts of the Australian 22 Squadron that were also droning over the Owen Stanleys toward Buna.

Less than an hour after the fighter planes left Port Moresby, a dozen B-26 mediums of the 22nd Bomb Group lumbered over the taxi strip of the main runway at 7 Mile Drome. The 12 Marauders roared down the airstrip and were airborne by 0900 hours. Col. Dwight Devine, commander of the 22nd, then jelled his B-26 units into three 4 plane diamonds and droned toward Buna. He knew his fighter escorts would catch up to him perhaps 50 miles from the Buna coast. Devine did not like to wait this long for escorts, but the P-39s would expend too much gasoline if they maintained a slow speed to stay with the B-26s during a flight to Buna.

Not until 0930 hours did the whine of P-39s

from the 8th Fighter Group's 80th Squadron echo from 12 Mile Drome. Col. Boyd Buzz Wagner led sixteen Aircobras toward the main runway. The aircraft were loaded with .50 caliber strafing belts and 37mm cannon shells. At 1032, the green light blinked from the control tower and Wagner, with his wingman, raced down the runway and took off. Fifteen more P-39s followed Wagner, and within ten minutes the sixteen American fighter planes were zooming over the Owen Stanley Mountains. They expected to catch up to Devine's Marauders in a half hour—unless they met Japanese Zeros before they reached the B-26s.

Earlier, as the Japanese convoy neared Buna through the Solomon Sea, Cmdr. Kusen Tai, the convoy commander aboard destroyer *Samidare,* had called Lae. "Send escorts in the event the Allied air forces attempt to harass our landing at Buna."

Capt. Masahisa Saito had already guessed that Allied recon planes had spotted the convoy and the Allies would attempt to attack the ships. So he had anticipated the need to defend the convoy as the ships approached Buna, and he had alerted his fighter pilots to prepare for air cover duty.

Masahisa would use two squadrons from his Tinian Wing to protect the Buna convoy, leading 12 Squadron himself, while Lieutenant Commander Nakajima relieved him with 11 Squadron two hours later. All aircraft at Lae had been loaded with fuel, 7.7 machine gun strafing belts, and 20mm cannon shells. Besides these two squadrons, Saito had also ordered Lt. Junichi Sasai to lead 36 Zeros of his 10 Squadron into the Owen Stanleys to patrol the Allied air routes from Moresby.

"We will attack any aircraft at Buna," Saito said, "and you will attack any aircraft that attempt to cross the mountains."

"Yes, Honorable Saito," Sasai answered, disappointed. He had hoped to join the formations going to Buna where expected action would take place. Sasai could not guess that he would find plenty of fighting himself over the Owen Stanleys.

Captain Saito kept his Zero squadrons at Salamaua on alert to reinforce 12 and 10 Squadrons over Buna if needed. And since Saito intended to keep Zeros over the convoy all day, perhaps he would ask these Salamaua squadrons to relieve the 10 and 12 Squadrons.

At 0830 hours, while Colonel Davies' 3rd Bomb Group, twelve planes, was droning over the Owen Stanleys, 36 Zeros of 12 Squadron zoomed down their jungle airstrip at Lae and soared into the northern sky. Over Huon Gulf, beyond Lae, the Zeros banked 90 degrees, southwest, and then droned toward Buna. A half hour later, Lt. Junuchi Sasai zoomed down the same Lae Airstrip, leading 36 Mitsubishi fighters of 10 Squadron. Soon the Zeros were droning southeast over the Owen Stanleys.

If the Americans counted many experienced and courageous pilots on their rolls, men like Davies, Strickland, Wagner, or Lynch, so too could the Japanese list many experienced and brave pilots. Besides such air leaders as Saito, Makajima and Sasai, The Tinian Fighter Wing numbered among its rolls some of the best fighter pilots who ever flew for Japan.

P/1c Hiroyashi Nishazawa of 11 Squadron had been a fighter pilot for only a few months. However, by the time he joined the Tinian Wing in Lae, in June of 1942, he had already downed more than 20 enemy planes, including a dozen American aircraft in the Philippines and in Java. Before his career ended, he would score 103 aerial victories, the highest of any Japanese pilot.

Nishazawa was a tall, thin man, with a perpetually gaunt look on his ever sober countenance. His thin face was pale most of the time and, at 140 pounds, his ribs protruded through his skin. He looked more like a man who needed a hospital bed than an aggressive fighter pilot. When he joined the Tinian Wing he never mingled with other pilots, never joked with them, and never smiled. He kept continually to himself, unfriendly and cold. Sometimes he spent an entire day speaking to no one, disdaining any overtures of friendship, and merely walking about like a cadaver with a zombie look in his dark eyes.

But once in the air, this strange man became an awesome genius. His aerobatics were breathtaking for he could make his plane respond unwaveringly to his sure, gentle touch of the controls. He seemed to have supernatural vision, for he could see enemy aircraft before anyone. His fellow pilots had dubbed him "The Devil," for in truth he showed a talent with a plane that only a supernatural creature could show.

P/1c Saburo Sakia, also of 11 Squadron, had brought with him to Lae years of experience as a successful fighter pilot. He had downed more than forty aircraft during two years of service in China, and another dozen kills during the opening months of the Pacific War. The Japanese claimed that Sakai had been the man who had brought down the famed Kelly and his B-17. Private Sakai was as outgoing and emotional as Nishizawa was cold and reserved. When Sakai lost a fellow pilot, he would brood for days before he bounced back with renewed eagerness to meet the enemy again. He had shown a remarkable skill in the Zero cockpit and he had already scored several kills in the New Guinea war.

Sakai was a man who had often disobeyed orders, flying off from his wingman to pursue enemy aircraft beyond the zones designated by his squadron leader. Still he had always succeeded and he never received more than mild reprimands for his disobedience to orders. Sakai would end the war as Japan's highest living air ace — with 64 victories.

P/1c Toshig Ota of 10 Squadron in the Tinian Wing was perhaps the most amiable pilot in the 24th Air Flotilla. He always indulged in fun and activities, he could laugh at a joke, and he was quick to make jokes of his own. He had the knack to bring a smile to fellow pilots in the drab, monotonous life at Lae. But once in the air, Ota sobered quickly and he devoted full attention to business. He had become so adept that Lt. Junichi Sasai had selected him as the squadron leader's wing man. Ota would score 85 victories, and in fact, he had already scored more than 80 kills since entering combat in China in 1938. But Toshig Ota would not survive the war to boast of his feats.

Thus did the air principals drone on to their confrontation around Buna and over the Owen Stanleys: Capt. Masahisa Saito and 36 planes, Lt. Junichi Sasai with 36 planes, and Lieutenant Commander Nakajima in reserve with 36 planes. For the Americans: Col. Bob Davies with 12 planes, Col. Dwight Devine with 12 B-26s, Lt. Frank Lukis with 12 Beauforts: Among the fighters: Capt. Tom Lynch with 16 P-39s, Col. Buzz Wagner with 16 Airacobras, and Lt. Larry Jackson with 12 P-40s.

As usual, the Allies would be outnumbered, but not by much this time. Saito droned eastward over the Solomon Sea and Sasai droned southeast over the Owen Stanleys. The Allied aircraft droned almost due north. In one hour, one group of adversaries would meet near disaster.

CHAPTER FIVE

At 0900, on 12 September, in the partly clouded skies, the 3rd Bomb Group, with the 35th Fighter Group escorts some 2,000 feet above them, crossed the coast off Buna and droned over the Solomon Sea. Less than 20 minutes later, Col. John Davies spotted the fleet of Japanese ships steaming toward Papua's north coast.

The five small maru freighters carried supplies for both the Yokoyama Force already in New Guinea and for the Yazawa Force that would soon follow from Rabaul. Vehicles and construction materials crammed the decks of two freighters, while stores of ammunition, food, medicine and other supplies filled the holds of other marus. The small vessels were also carrying animals, detachments of troops and New Britain native carriers.

When Cmdr. Kusen Tai, aboard the flag destroyer *Samidare*, saw the approaching aircraft, he ordered all men to battle stations. Moments later, the vessels scattered in several directions and anti-aircraft gunners sent spews of ack-ack fire at the oncoming planes. Bursts of flak dotted the sky with huge black puffs, but Col. John Davies never wavered. He personally led his lead three plane V of B-25s toward the freighter *Kotoku Maru* and he then called Maj. Bob Strickland.

"Bob," Davies told the 89th Squadron leader, "take your A-24s after the destroyers; we'll take the marus with our B-25s."

"Roger," the major answered.

A moment later, the six Mitchells zoomed after the scurrying marus, the pilots barely able to see the vessels through the heavy smoke from huffing stacks and the continual black puffs from ack-ack bursts.

Still Davies droned forward and at a height of 3,000 feet he unloosed his bombs over the *Kotoku Maru*. However, two of the 500 pounders landed short, erupting geysers of blue tropical water. The other two bombs struck squarely on the fore deck of the maru, shuddered the ship violently, and then brought a pall of smoke from the freighter's deck. The vessel tilted to port while whoop alarms blared through the ship and echoed across the Solomon Sea.

The next B-25, following Davies, also pounced on the suddenly burning ship and sent four more 500 pounders toward the crippled vessel. Three of the bombs missed but the fourth hit squarely on the port quarter, ripping a huge hole in the vessel's hull before sea water poured into the maru and brought an uncontrollable list. Cmdr. Kusen Tai granted the maru's commander a request to abandon ship.

Unfortunately for the 3rd Group, the *Kotoku Maru* became their only victim. The four other B-25s dumped their bombs over other marus, but only scored near misses. Meanwhile, the six A-24 Dauntlesses, with their mere two bomb loads, had little success against the heavy firing, swiftly zig-zagging destroyers. The A-24s scored only minor hits or near misses, nothing that had even slowed down any of the destroyers. In fact, the *Samidare* gunners brought down one of the A-24s, the aircraft plopping fatally into the sea.

The 3rd Group complement of planes had simply been too few. They could not deliver enough bombs to cause major damage, particularly since Japanese helmsmen had learned to deftly maneuver their vessels against medium or high level aerial attacks. The only consolation: the 3rd Bomb Group had rattled Commander Tai, especially with the loss of the *Kotoku Maru*. Tai ordered all vessels to the northward, away from the Buna beaches.

But Davies cursed. He had the convoy on the run, but his aircraft had expended their bombs. He searched the sky, looking for the Beauforts of 22 Squadron. But the Australians were nowhere in sight. Davies now mustered his planes for strafing runs over the fleeing Japanese ships, hoping some of their tracer fire could set off magazines or gasoline explosions to perhaps sink more of the Japanese vessels. He had barely started after the convoy when he got a frantic call from his wingman.

"Colonel! Bandits at three o'clock; three o'clock."

John Davies peered from his B-25 cabin and when he saw the specks to the west, at least 35 or 40 Zeros, possibly two squadrons, he felt a chill. Davies scanned the skies, hoping to find his escorts, but he saw no sign of the 35th Group's P-39s. The Airacobras had apparently become separated from the 3rd Bomb Group. Davies was no coward, but he could not engage in an aerial battle with two squadrons of fighter planes, not his slower bombers carrying only gunners with twin .50 caliber guns. There would be no contest against the darting, zooming Zeros with their six 7.7 machine guns and 20 mm cannons.

"All pilots," Davies cried into his radio. "Bandits! Swarms of them! Let's get the hell out of here."

Both the six B-25s and the five A-24s banked in a wide 180 degree turn and then zoomed at full speed to the south, hoping to cross the Owen Stanleys before the Zeros spotted them.

Only after the bombers disappeared to the south did Capt. Tom Lynch and his P-39 pilots come out of a cloud bank to find no sign of the 3rd Group. Lynch assumed the 3rd Group was heading for home and he decided to hurry southward to catch up to the bombers. He cried into his radio: "All pilots: bandits may be on the way and the Reapers are gone. We'll head south and catch up to the 3rd Group."

The P-39s also banked in wide 180 degree turns and roared southward. But the Japanese would find the Reapers first.

One of the vanguard Japanese pilots of 12 Squadron spotted the American bombers veering southward toward the Owen Stanley mountains and he immediately called his flight leader, to report them. The leader, in turn, called Capt. Masahisa Saito, who was leading the entire Zero formations.

"Honorable Saito, one of my pilots has seen American aircraft to the south."

Captain Saito squinted to the south until he too saw the 3rd Group planes. Saito saw no sign of fighter plane escorts so he correctly assumed that the bombers had lost their fighter plane protectors. Saito knew that the bombers would fly straight to Port Moresby and the Tinian Wing commander saw a good chance to catch the American planes with his speedier Zeros before the planes crossed the mountains. Saito immediately altered course on a diagonal route to cut down the distance between his own and the American formations.

"All pilots," Saito radioed his pilots, "we will pursue the Yankee bombers. Fourth Flight will remain at twelve thousand feet behind the others to intercept any enemy fighter planes that might interfere. Twelve Squadron pilots will follow me."

The cagey Captain Saito had guessed correctly.

He caught up to the A-24s and B-25s only fifty miles south of Buna. This 12 September morning would always be known as the "Day of the Reaper Disaster."

The eager Zero pilots, astounded to see the bombers without escorts, peeled off ecstatically and dove toward the bombers. At 0920, one Tinian pilot unleashed the first burst of strafing fire into the American bombers. The American pilots veered and banked, rose and dove, or twisted and turned to avoid the Zero fighters, but all to no avail. Pairs of Zero fighters waded into the slow moving, less maneuverable bombers, sending deadly streams of tracer and 20mm fire into wings, tails, fuselages, and engines of the eleven 3rd Group bombers. The responding turret gun fire did little against the heavy barrages from the fast moving, quick darting Zeros. The chattering gunfire reverberated across the sky like incessant thunder, and the roar of planes echoed through the mountains like the din of squealing lorrie birds.

Within five minutes, the Zeros had taken a heavy toll. An A-24 blew up after a stream of Zero fire struck the fuel tanks and ignited the volatile gasoline. A pair of 20mm shells from a second Zero sliced away the left wing of a second A-24, as though the shells had been some kind of giant ax. The Dauntless simply rolled over and plunged dizzily into the depths of the Owen Stanley range. An array of .30 caliber hits shredded the tail assembly of a third A-24 until the tail simply fell off and the aircraft cartwheeled into the mountainous jungle below.

The bombers were helpless, although one B-25 gunner did hit a Zero that disintegrated in mid-air.

Still another 3rd Group A-24 met death before the nightmare ended. Zero fire riddled the Dauntless into a flaming wreck that simply fell out of the sky in cascading fire. Also, two of the B-25s took so many hits, the Mitchells could no longer stay aloft and they dizzily spun downward to disappear into the forested jungles below. Even those planes that remained airborne did not escape the murderous Japanese aerial assault. The remaining B-25s had also suffered serious damage, along with the death of two gunners. As the aircraft staggered back to Moresby, one damaged aircraft could not scale the Owen Stanleys, and the B-25 flew on to Milne Bay for an emergency landing. Only one plane, Maj. Bob Strickland's surviving A-24, had escaped damage.

Col. Bob Davies finally found thick cloud banks and led his survivors into the dense mists to avoid further punishment. The Zero pilots were eager to continue after the Americans, but Captain Saito refused. He did not want any collisions in the dense blind clouds that could kill some of his pilots.

In the near slaughter, one of the pilots had downed two of the A-24s and a second eager pilot had downed one of the Mitchells. Captain Saito had downed the second Mitchell, while other Tinian Wing pilots had downed the other two A-24s.

Meanwhile, Capt. Tom Lynch and his P-39 pilots never saw the Zeros; nor did the Japanese fighter pilots see the Airacobras. In fact, the 35th Group returned to Port Moresby without firing a shot.

The Australians, meanwhile, never came near the convoy. Uncannily, the Australian commander of the Aussie squadrons had told A/C Frank Lukis to forget the Buna convoy and to go after some troop laden barges coming down from Salamaua to Buna. "These troops are more important," the air commander had told Air Commander Lukis. The Beauforts and Kittyhawks had done just that, and in fact, they had done a good job, sinking four of six barges. Still the Australians had left the American bombers exposed and the Buna supply convoy almost intact.

After Captain Saito smashed the 3rd Bomb Group, he led his Zero pilots over the Buna coast and out to the Solomon Sea. Saito arrived over the convoy just as the *Kotoku Maru* belched its last bubbly gasp before disappearing into the water. However small barges from Buna were already skimming out to pick up survivors. They would pluck from the sea 363 men of the engineer and infantry companies aboard the maru, thus saving most of the 400 men.

With the skies now empty of aircraft, Captain Saito radioed Cmdr. Kusen Tai and told him to reverse course and continue to Buna with the other four marus. "It is our understanding," Saito said, "that the supplies and animals you carry are badly needed by the Yokoyama Forces if they are to continue their drive to Port Moresby. You are also carrying the supplies for the remainder of the Nankai Shitai Force, is that not so?"

"Yes, Captain," the convoy commander answered.

"Then proceed at once to Buna," Saito barked. "We regret the loss of the maru, but your other vessels do not appear undully damaged. I assure you, the Tinian Wing will provide air cover all day. We will be patrolling the skies in relays."

Somewhat embarrassed, but obviously safe now, Cmdr. Kusen Tai turned about and continued his sail to Buna.

As the convoy neared the coast, a dozen B-26s of the 22nd Bomb Group loomed out of the Owen Stanleys and roared toward the ships. Once more Commander Tai scattered his vessels as Col. Dwight Devine led his Marauders over the vessels. The descending bombs did little damage, for Japanese helmsmen easily avoided most of the bombs from a 6,000 feet altitude. But the 22nd Group was not so lucky. As they were completing their runs, a swarm of Zeros came from the west, Lt. Cmdr. Tadashi Nakajima and the pilots of his 11 Squadron. Colonel Devine looked frantically overhead for his P-39 escorts, but saw no sign of them. He then broke off his attack on the convoy, veered quickly in 180 degrees and led his Marauders swiftly southward.

The B-26s could not outrun the Zeros. Within five minutes, 11 Squadron was on top of them. Within seconds the sober faced Nishizawa, "The

Devil," knocked one of the B-26s out of the air. A twin attack by Lieutenant Commander Nakajima himself and P/1c Saburo Sakai knocked another Marauder down in flames. No doubt, Devine's formations would have been possibly annihilated, but luckily the 22nd Group commander found a cloud bank and ducked his B-26s into the dense patch of mist before the Zeros ate him up.

Pilots like Sakai and Nishizawa were ready to follow the B-26s into the cloud bank, but Lieutenant Commander Nakajima refused to let them go. They might crash into each other in such misty blindness.

Devine was grateful to escape the Zero assault, but he felt utterly frustrated. Where were the P-39 escorts that were supposed to meet him over Buna? Devine did not know it, but the 8th Fighter Group had run into the Tinian Wing 11 Squadron under Lt. Junichi Sasai.

Boyd Buzz Wagner's 16 P-39s of the 8th Group's 80th Squadron was still a half hour from his rendezvous with the B-26s when a swarm of planes had loomed from the sky to the northwest. Wagner had cried into his radio. "Bandits! Eleven o'clock high! We've got a fight; wingmen stay close."

Capt. Masahisa Saito had guessed right when he suspected that the Allies would send more than the 3rd Group to hit the Buna convoy, and he knew that enemy escort planes generally left base a half hour later to catch up to the bombers. So the Tinian Wing commander had wisely sent

Lieutenant Sasai to the Allied air route from Moresby. When Lieutenant Sasai spotted the 8th Group P-39s, he grinned, for he and his pilots of 10 Squadron were itching for a fight, and Sasai had twice the number of planes against the inferior Airacobra. He radioed his pilots.

"Enemy aircraft at two o'clock, low. We shall attack in pairs."

Within minutes the 36 Zeros dove toward the American fighter planes. When Sasai closed on the 8th Fighter Group, he cried again into his radio: "Remember, Wingmen will remain together and attack in pairs." Then: "Banzai!"

The whine of straining engines echoed above the Owen Stanleys before the chatter of machine guns and the whoosh of 20mm cannon fire from Zeros rumbled across the sky. Buzz Wagner made no attempt to run. He could not, for the faster Zeros could easily catch his P-39s. He picked up his radio.

"We've got a fight," he said again. "In pairs — pick your targets."

The American pilots also banked their planes, their engines also screaming above the mountainous jungles. American machine gun fire and 37mm shells also rolled across the sky. As usual, the Japanese outnumbered the Americans and their Zeros were more maneuverable. Within minutes, the Tinian Wing pilots knocked four of the American planes out of the air.

Lt. Junichi Sasai got two of the planes himself. He had maneuvered behind one of the P-39s, chasing the darting, banking American aircraft like a shadow, his four guns spitting deadly fire and his 20mm cannon spitting fatal shells. Sasai's fire had ripped away one Airacobra's tail and the P-39 had simply dropped like a dead bird into the dense trees below. The Japanese squadron leader had next caught a P-39 that had attempted to get away. He had sent a stream of .30 caliber fire into the cockpit, killing the American pilot before the P-39 spun dizzily to earth.

P/1c Toshig Ota also got a P-39. An American pilot had flown low, streaking desperately, but Ota streaked after him, spewing .30 caliber fire and 20mm shells that riddled the P-39 fuselage. When the American pilot banked his plane up and to the right, Ota followed quickly and instinctively. He had caught the fuselage of the P-39 with two shells that tore apart the engine. The nose of the Airacobra exploded and the P-39 had fallen tail over nose before the flaming plane spun to earth in a fatal crash.

Another Zero pilot caught Buzz Wagner in his sights and sent streams of tracers into the P-39, puncturing the Airacobra fuselage with several hits. Wagner could not shake the Zero but, in desperation, he tried another tactic. The colonel violently throttled his plane, slowing the aircraft abruptly, while the Japanese plane zoomed past him. Before the Zero pilot recovered from this unexpected maneuver, Wagner was on his tail and the colonel sent a heavy chatter of .50 caliber strafing fire into the lightly armored plane. The Zero simply exploded and the pieces fluttered into the jungle ridges below.

The zooming, darting, skittering dogfight had prevailed for a half hour before both sides expended ammunition and both commanders broke off the fight. Buzz Wagner had done his best, but he had again come out on the short end of a dogfight. He lost five of his P-39s and suffered damage to five more. Conversely, the Japanese only lost two planes. Worst of all, Wagner had failed to meet and protect Dwight Devine's B-26s because the Japanese had intercepted him and his pilots.

As he flew back to Moresby with his crippled P-39 formation, Buzz Wagner cursed under his breath. The same story: not enough pilots, not enough aircraft, and no planes capable of matching the superior Japanese Zero.

Lt. Junichi Sasai, in turn, flew back toward Lae with smug satisfaction. He had again defeated the Americans. The 10 Squadron commander, in fact, still ached for more action, as all winners do, and he called Masahisa Saito.

"Honored Captain, we have driven off a squadron of Yankee aircraft after we destroyed some half dozen of them. I believe they intended to escort bombers going to Buna. Should we fly on to Buna to seek these bombers?"

"There is no need," Captain Saito said, "for we have already dealt with the Yankee bombers. You may return to Lae."

"Yes, Captain," Sasai answered, disappointed.

By late afternoon, the Japanese convoy anchored off the coast of Buna and barges spent the next 14 hours carrying tons of supplies, food, ammunition, and guns ashore. The barges also carried ashore the 170 horses and 700 Rabaul natives who would be used as jungle carriers.

Within a few days, General Horii would have the supplies he needed to continue the Japanese drive on Port Moresby.

When the remnants of Col. John Davies' group returned to Port Moresby, where two of the planes were forced to belly in, Gen. Ennis Whitehead was shocked at the heavy losses in aircraft. He was also quite dismayed at the failure of the 35th Fighter Group to cling to the 3rd Group. He was further upset because Buzz Wagner had run into a swarm of Zeros. And finally, the 5th Air Force ADVON commander was bitter when he learned that the RAAF aircraft had gone up the coast to attack barges instead of joining in the attack on the Buna convoy. Perhaps the P-40s of the 75 Squadron could have prevented the heavy losses to the 3rd Bomb Group.

When General Whitehead learned that the 9th RAAF Group commander in New Guinea had diverted his 75 and 22 Squadrons to attack barges, Whitehead called the 9th's commander to his office where he angrily dressed down the Australian and relieved him of command.

"I told you I was running this show," Whitehead barked, "and no airman in this command does anything without my permission. You get your ass out of New Guinea. I'll ask General Kenney to send me somebody who knows he can't do as he goddamn pleases. The air war up here is tough enough, and we just can't afford to have anything less than total cooperation."

Strangely, no one in Brisbane complained of Whitehead's decision to summarily discharge the 9th RAAF air commander. The decision left a strong impression on Air Commander Lukis, Lt. Larry Jackson, and even American airmen. They saw that Whitehead meant what he said, when he had issued that directive: "Any man who fails to follow my instructions will be immediately relieved of duty and court-martialed." However, the 9th commander was not court-martialed.

Meanwhile, after the successful discharge of men, animals, and supplies from the Buna convoy, and after the American aerial defeat over Buna, Gen. Tomitaro Horii called his staff together at Ioribaiwa. "Our troops have rested and we will soon have more supplies than we need. We are ready to descend Imita Ridge and deliver our hammer blow on Port Moresby. I have sent out scouts to probe the Australian defenses and they have brought back favorable reports."

Col. Yosuke Yokoyama now agreed with the Nankai Shitai commander. The men *were* rested, some supplied *had* arrived, and the prospect of more supplies arriving seemed certain.

Both Gen. Douglas MacArthur and Gen. Basil Morris were quite sure that Horii would soon continue his drive to Moresby. Morris longed for the Australian combat brigades and the 32nd American Infantry Division that were still in Australia. He had few transport ships to move men and supplies to New Guinea by sea, and Kenney's transport aircraft could only move a minimum of men and supplies. With the critical situation, Morris offered MacArthur a stunning proposal: they must use the airmen and service troops at Port Moresby to defend this Allied base. MacArthur agreed. They met with Gen. George Kenney and Gen. "Bent-Nose" Whitehead.

"Our position is critical," MacArthur said. "We may need to use your airmen to fight a ground war if the Japanese attempt to reach Moresby."

Whitehead shook his head. "General, sir, there's no way we can afford to lose valuable combat flyers and trained ground crews. We could never replace them. Anyway, they'd be no match for those Japanese jungle fighters."

"We simply can't get replacements up here fast enough," Morris said.

"But those airmen are not combat troops," Whitehead insisted.

"I'm sorry, Ennis," MacArthur said, "but if those Japanese come over Imita Ridge, every soldier in Moresby will need to use a gun. I've asked General Morris to send drill cadres to every air and service unit to train men in infantry tactics."

"Cadres will come from our depleted Australian 39 Battalion who have a wealth of experience in jungle fighting," General Morris told Whitehead. "They'll do a good job."

But Whitehead was bitterly dismayed and he now looked at Kenney, a plea in Whitehead's eyes. However, Kenney shook his head. "You can't believe how this hurts me, Ennis. But in all honesty, I've got to agree with Generals MacArthur and Morris. We have no alternative. We couldn't even evacuate Port Moresby for lack of enough shipping."

"We'll have submarines lying off shore," General MacArthur told Whitehead. "If it appears that Port Moresby is lost, we'll evacuate as many of your 5th Air Force personnel as we can." He paused. "As General Morris said, the cadres are well experienced. They'll do a good job. Send a directive to all units, Ennis. The Australians will start at once to give your airmen instructions in jungle fighting."

"Yes sir," Whitehead answered glumly.

Despite his objections, Whitehead knew that MacArthur, Morris, and Kenney were right: By this third week in September, 1942, the war in New Guinea had indeed reached a crisis.

CHAPTER SIX

On 13 September, the day after the disastrous mission against the Buna convoy, Gen. George Kenney could only count on 83 bombers, 108 fighter planes, and 72 transport planes in all of his 5th Air Force. Among the bomb groups, the 3rd had 26 A-20s and five B-25s, the 22nd had 14 B-26s, the 43rd had ten B-17s, the 90th had twelve B-27s, and the Australian 22 Squadron had sixteen A-20s. Among the fighter units, the 8th had 38 P-39s, the 35th had 32 P-39s, the Aussie 30 Squadron in Milne Bay had 16 Beaufighters, and the Aussie 75 Squadron had 22 P-40s at Port Moresby. Kenney could not count on the 49th U.S. Fighter Group aricraft, whose P-40s were needed in Darwin, Australia against Japanese air attacks from Java.

Conversely, the 24th Air Flotilla had in New

Guinea alone over a hundred Zeros at Lae and another 50 at Salamaua, along with 40 to 50 Val dive bombers of Shingo's B Group in Buna. Fifty Betty bombers from Shingo's A Group were in Gasmata. Further, Admiral Kasaka was sending new Betty and Val bombers to Arawe on New Britain's south coast, across the Solomon Sea from the north coast of Papua New Guinea. Besides the 250 aircraft already committed to the fight in New Guinea, Kasaka could draw on two to three hundred more fighters and bombers out of Rabaul.

However, despite the obvious air superiority, the Japanese became victims of their own naivete. They had known nothing but victory after victory, conquest after conquest. Once their air power had destroyed enemy airfields, such fields never recovered and Japanese ground troops, without enemy air interference, easily finished the job of conquering certain areas: Malaysia, the Philippines, the East Indies, Java, New Britain, and much of New Guinea. All Japanese commanders in the Southwest Pacific, from Gen. Hitoshi Imamura on down, never considered the possibility that American industrial might was in full swing.

The Japanese had done quite a thorough job on Port Moresby during the 11 August air strikes and they had done considerable damage in subsequent strikes. But they had foolishly believed that these strikes had adequately eliminated Port Moresby as an effective air base. Admiral Kasaka had not considered American industry and technology. If Washington was slow in sending combat hardware to New Guinea, they were quite speedy in sending construction and service equipment to the Southwest Pacific. In fact, the most active people in the Pacific by mid 1942 were Navy seabees and Army construction battalions. Despite air raids on Port Moresby, by mid-September the Americans had more bulldozers, machine shops, caterpillars, cranes, and other heavy equipment in New Guinea than one would likely see on a freeway construction site in California.

The Americans could now build or repair airdromes in hours where the Japanese needed days or weeks to do the same thing. So the Japanese were thinking in terms of their own ability to recover from bombing raids, rather than American ability. The Japanese 8th Area Forces commanders thus wallowed in wishful thinking, especially since the 24th Air Flotilla had done a quite thorough job against the 3rd, 22nd, and 8th American air groups that had tried to stop the Buna convoy on 12 September. No one in the Japanese camp fully realized that by the fall of 1942 the Americans had the equipment and engineers they had sorely lacked during the earlier months of the war.

The Americans also had another item the Japanese lacked—individual ingenuity. The Japanese did not realize that dedicated American free thinkers, especially in desperate situations, commonly improvised to compensate for a lack of military hardware. Such Americans often came up with innovative techniques that startled combat air crews, who nonetheless willingly tried such innovations if there was a possibility of success.

The Japanese failure to keep the Port Moresby runways out of commission, and their failure to recognize unorthodox methods in the American military would prove disastrous for the Japanese—even in this mid-September when every man in the Southwest Pacific fully expected the Japanese to capture Port Moresby.

Among the most notorious of the American innovators in the Southwest Pacific was Maj. Paul "Pappy" Gunn, a 45 year old, ex-commercial airline owner who had run away from home at age 16 to join the U.S. Navy air arm in 1917. After a 20 year naval career he had retired to the Philippines where he bought and directed the Inter-Island Airlines, operating out of the Philippines.

When war broke out in 1941, Gunn joined the U.S. Army Air Force with the rank of captain and he soon put his best talent to work—salvaging and repairing wrecked aircraft. The round faced, pot-bellied Mad Professor Gunn had escaped from the Philippines in early 1942 and he eventually joined the 3rd Bomb Group as the unit's engineering officer. Although assigned to the 3rd Group, Pappy Gunn had spent much of his time with other units repairing aircraft. Since March of 1942, Paul "Mad Professor" Gunn had put back into flying condition more than a hundred planes that other air engineers said could never fly again.

The Mad Professor had established a graveyard of wrecked planes in Port Moresby, the biggest junk yard west of San Francisco. Gunn had initiated the custom of cannibalizing, wherein he would use the parts of the most seriously damaged aircraft to repair the less damaged. Air commanders had a common refrain for their airmen: "Just get the plane home; Pappy Gunn and his jackal crews will get the plane flying again."

Gunn had often improvised parts in his makeshift machine shop: an aircraft tail from a piece of wing, a new engine cowl from a piece of fuselage, a cabin window from the plexiglass of a gun turret; or he'd improvise tractor wheels for aircraft wheels, truck brakes for aircraft brakes, or jeep seats for gunners seats. Many an Allied aircraft flying over the Owen Stanley Mountains resembled a street urchin with patched denims; or the aircraft carried improvised infantry machine guns in the place of hard-to-find aerial guns.

When John Davies mustered his dozen planes on 12 September for the strike on the Buna convoy, half of these planes had been salvaged and restored by Gunn.

Pappy Gunn was supposedly subject to the orders of superiors, but the independent minded, imaginative Mad Professor invariably did as he pleased. His ability to salvage wrecked planes was so phenomenal that nobody questioned his activities. Rumor said he once got spare parts out of Brisbane at the point of a gun and he had once stolen a dozen bombsights out of the Melbourne Air Depot for the 3rd Group's B-25s.

During the latter part of August and into September, the pot bellied officer with the perpetual twinkle in his steel blue eyes and the constant optimism on his round face was conducting himself in a most unorthodox manner. He was working on some 3rd Group A-20s, an aircraft commanders in Europe did not want because the Havoc was considered too lightly armed and too slow to support ground troops. So the A-20 was one plane quite readily available to the 5th Air Force.

Pilots had complained that the twin .50 caliber guns in the nose lacked the fire power to kill jungle snakes, much less enemy troops. Also the Havoc's gas tanks were too small, barely enabling an A-20 to fly to Buna and back. Gunn had concocted a strange innovation for the A-20 that would change the Havoc into a deadly attack bomber. He had installed four .50 caliber guns in place of the two nose guns and he had installed two more .50 caliber guns in the wings. He had also installed a 450 gallon auxiliary gas tank in the bomb bay to increase the aircraft's range. Gunn himself has tested the modified A-20 off the coast of Moresby and the aircraft had responded satisfactorily to the new design.

"Okay, Johnny," Gunn told Col. John Davies on 13 September, "now you've got a strafing plane that can cause some real damage."

"Sure," Davies scowled. "We got six heavy guns to knock down trees at low level, but no bomb bay to carry bombs."

"We've got another innovation, too," Pappy

Gunn grinned. Gunn, in fact, had enlisted the aid of the 5th Air Force commander, himself, Gen. George Kenney.

When 5th Air Force brass complained that Pappy Gunn was conducting strange experiments in New Guinea instead of doing his job, Gen. George Kenney himself flew up to New Guinea to find out what the Mad Professor was up to. When Gunn told the general what he was trying to do with the A-20, Kenney immediately approved, for the 5th Air Force commander agreed that tactical air support was the most important function for 5th Air Force. Then, when Gunn told Kenney he didn't know what to do about the reduced bomb bay capacity, Kenney's eyes brightened, the first time he had shown any emotion since coming to Australia.

Kenney, while a major at Wright Field, Ohio, during the early 30s had been working on a means to drop bombs at low altitudes without having fragments of the explosion hit the aircraft. Kenney had devised a 23 pound canister fragmentation bomb, with a supersensitive fuse and attached to a parachute. When the bomb dropped, even at ground level, the parachute opened, giving the plane time to get away before the bomb hit and exploded. The bomb would explode into a thousand pieces and could penetrate a four inch plank. The Army Air Force had produced nearly 10,000 of these parafrags but they had been stored away and forgotten.

When Kenney won command of the SWPA air forces, he had ordered anything he could to follow him, including the 10,000 parafrags that nobody wanted. Kenney had hoped that somehow these little bombs might be useful in the jungles.

"You won't need a bomb bay, Pappy," Kenney told Gunn. "You can attach a honeycomb rack under the bomb bay and fit in these parafrags. Not only will your A-20 be able to strafe at treetop level, but also drop bombs from this height; and you'll be able to keep the auxiliary tank in the bomb bay."

"General, you've solved my problem," Mad Professor Gunn grinned.

Thus Paul Pappy Gunn devised the honeycomb rack.

Now at Moresby, Col. John Davies frowned, puzzled by Gunn's answer. "What the hell do you mean, you've got another innovation?"

"Take a look under the bomb bay," Gunn said. "We'll use a new type of bomb, a cluster of small bombs attached to parachutes so you can bomb right at tree top level. That's the most important job here in the Pacific—hitting enemy ground units, airfields, supply dumps, supporting Aussie ground troops. You know that medium height bombing isn't any goddamn good on those jungle positions under dense trees. At best, it's a hit or miss proposition. If you can bomb at treetop level, you'll improve your accuracy one hundred percent. I figure the rack can carry maybe forty or fifty frag bombs. When you release them, the small parachute opens and the bombs float slowly to earth. These parafrag clusters will be ideal for hitting troop concentrations, vehicles, guns, armor, or aircraft on the ground."

"I never heard of anything like that," Davies said. "Where the hell did you get those things? Anyway, we'd need thousands of them."

"Well, Johnny," Gunn grinned, "General Kenney himself brought ten thousand of them with him to Australia and he's ordering a hundred thousand more. Come on, I'll show you how it works."

Colonel Davies skeptically went along for the ride to witness Paul Gunn's test. They flew a simulated low level bombing and strafing run over the trees of a remote patch of jungle in eastern New Guinea. Davies wasn't sure he'd come back alive, but the colonel was astonished when the heavy blast from six .50 caliber guns almost tore away the trees. Then Davies gaped in amazement as three dozen parafrags dropped from the aircraft at an altitude of less than 200 feet, barely above the treetops, and drifted lazily to earth like descending white umbrellas. The A-20 easily cleared the area before the staccato of explosions erupted from the length of the jungle.

"My God, Pappy, I don't believe it."

"Think what you can do, Johnny," Gunn grinned. "You can get right on top of a bridge, or a line of parked aircraft, or a column of troops on the trail, or even jungle hidden supply dumps and troop concentrations. You'll be able to strafe and bomb at the same time; knock hell out of them."

"Goddamn," John Davies returned the grin. "What the hell will those Nips think when they see a Havoc come down their throats on a straf-ing and bombing run?"

"I've got four Havocs modified now," Gunn said, "and I'll modify the rest. But," he gestured, "this is nothing. Wait till you see the B-25s. We'll have four of them ready in a few days."

"B-25s?" Davies cried.

"Sure," Gunn nodded. "It'll be a commerce de-stroyer, with more low level fire power than any-body ever saw. They promised us new B-25s, didn't they? Well, we'll turn those medium Mitchells into low level attack planes, and with a hell of a lot more power than the A-20. I'm pull-ing the bombardier compartment in the nose and putting in six guns, along with four more guns on the fuselage. You'll be able to carry a hundred frags in the bomb bays. Then we'll pull out the ball turret and put in an extra auxiliary gas tank. You'll be able to fly that Mitchell six-seven hun-dred miles one way."

"You're crazy," Davies huffed. "Christ, there's no way anybody can fly a Mitchell with that kind of armament at tree top level."

"Johnny," Gunn pointed, "the only goddamn planes you can expect out here are A-20s and B-25s. If that's all we get, then we'll have to alter them to fit this jungle war out here."

John Davies did not answer.

"We don't have railroad yards and factories to bomb in the jungle," Gunn continued, "so who needs a goddamn bombardier? Who needs a ball turret? What the hell can a belly gunner do from three to five thousand feet? Sure, he's supposed to fight off Zeros, but did you ever see one of those bastards come at you from underneath? No. They always come from the flank or from upstairs." He paused and grinned again. "I'll have the B-25s ready in a few days."

"Pappy," Davies said, "if you can do the same with a B-25 as you did with an A-20, we'll have a hell of a surprise for those sons 'a bitches."

Gunn grinned, banked the A-20 into an 180 degree turn, and a half hour later he had landed at Koki Drome. Davies immediately ordered his pilots to practice the low level technique on the A-20s, rotating his flyers between flying in combat and training in low level tactics. Davies also rotated his remaining A-20s from combat to revetment sites so that Gunn could convert these Havocs as he had the first four. Finally, he left his remaining B-25s in revetments so that Gunn could convert these to attack bombers.

Gen. George Kenney gave Paul Gunn full support and he had even ordered all light bomber pilots to practice the technique of using parafrags. He had even suggested that fighter pilots practice the technique. Kenney also ordered all engineering officers of the light bomber and fighter squadrons, Americans and Australians alike, to adapt honeycomb racks for their aircraft to use when needed.

RAAF airmen of the 75 P-40 and 22 Beaufort Australian Squadrons complained, aiming their barbs at Pappy Gunn, whose initiative had forced the new innovation. But these Australians, as well as Americans, got the word from Whitehead, who gave full support to the parafrag bomb effort. Despite grumbling by the American and Australian airmen in this mid-summer of 1942, they could not guess that Pappy Gunn's innovations would turn around the Papuan campaign.

By the last week in August, Pappy Gunn had completed the conversions of 22 3rd Group Havocs and by the week of 12 September he had converted the group's four B-25s, fitting 400 gallon gas tanks into the extracted ball turret area to give the Mitchell more range. American fighter units, as well as Australian units, meanwhile, had completed the job of adapting honeycomb racks for their aircraft, and many of the pilots has been instructed in the use of parafrags. Kenney would soon enough get rid of the 10,000 parafrags he had brought from the States.

Now Gunn was ready to test the B-25. Some of the air depot mechanics at Moresby grinned in amusement at the strange contraption: A B-25 with ten big guns jutting from the nose and fuselage. The Mad Professor had gone too far this time.

And in fact, when Pappy Gunn tried to test the obviously front heavy B-25, he could not get the plane off the ground. The Mitchell ran off the end of the runway and Gunn barely stopped the plane before it hit a clump of trees. Ground mechanics towed the weird B-25 back to a revetment area with a tractor. Then, the ground crew got out paint and brushes to neatly paint on the nose of the plane: "Pappy's Folly." They added a second touch of humor by painting a two gun cowboy on the nose who blasted away with six guns. When Gunn saw the artistry, his blue eyes twinkled, accepting the handiwork in good humor.

"All right you clowns," he told his mechanics, "you'll see."

"Major," the crew chief said, "there's no way you can get that monstrosity off the ground with an arsenal in the nose. You'll need to take out some of the guns."

"Like hell," Gunn huffed. "You heard of a navy tin can? Well, this plane will be an air corps tin can, a commerce destroyer."

The Mad Professor soon solved his problem. He moved the four side guns further back on the fuselage and he moved the auxiliary gas tank behind the wing to balance the center of gravity. He then took off again, with only one brave mechanic willing to fly with him. The Mitchell took off smoothly.

Gunn had succeeded in devising an aircraft that would become the backbone of the jungle war in the Pacific for the next two years.

However, despite Pappy Gunn's handiwork, the war in New Guinea was still perilous for the Allies. General Horii's 5,000 troops were regaining strength and securing supplies for the continued drive from Ioribaiwa. Further, Japanese aircraft were landing at Kokoda to unload more supplies for transshipment by foot down to Ioribaiwa. Horii guessed by the third week in September his men were fit and ready to go. New supplies from the Buna convoy had arrived from the north coast of Papua. More supplies had been flown into Kokoda and then carried southward to Ioribaiwa.

On the evening of 19 September, Gen. Tomitaro Horii called a meeting of his staff. "Prepare at once to move forward. We will strike the Australians at Imita Ridge on the morning of twenty-one September, two days from now. Are there any objections?"

None.

"Good," Horii nodded. "We will ready all units. Be sure they have ample supplies and ammunition."

The next morning, 20 September, Capt. Jim Hennebry called his 90th Squadron crews of the 3rd Bomb Group to a briefing. "You've all been trained in low level strikes, and we'll be making the first combat sortie with the new parafrag in about an hour. We've got charts from the Australians on the positions of those Japanese at Ioribaiwa, and we'll try to hit them hard." He looked at his watch: 0530. "We'll make the strike at about 0645 hours. This mission will be a real test."

"Yeh," one of the officers answered disdainfully. "It'll be a test all right. We'll either rattle hell out of them or get our ass shot off."

"Those are the chances," Hennebry said.

Personnel in Moresby had already been drilling for some days in jungle infantry tactics and they were tired. Still, they came out to 3 Mile Drome to stare curiously at these A-20s with the porcupine noses and honeycombs under the wings. The ground personnel watched the A-20s taxi along the 3 Mile Drome taxiway for take-off. They had not yet accustomed themselves to the strange sight of six guns jutting from the Havoc noses and wings, or with the honeycomb bomb racks that resembled huge, grotesque hives with some kind of weird, monstrous, white backed creatures clinging to the bellies of the A-20s.

For the pilots and gunners of the A-20s, apprehension prevailed. Yes, they had practiced low level parafrag strikes, but could the technique work in combat, where Japanese ack-ack guns could practically reach up and touch them? Within a half hour they would know.

At Ioribaiwa itself, Gen. Tomitaro Horii had received frequent reports from scouts that the Allies were training the service and air troops at Port Moresby to defend the big Allied base against a Japanese assault. The reports brought a grin to Horii's round face.

"They have surely reached the point of desperation," the Nankai Shitai commander said. "And surely, how could these Allied service troops fight against our experienced jungle fighters? We shall enjoy a grand victory in these circumstances."

At 0645 hours, 20 September, Jim Hennebry roared down 3 Mile Drome before his A-20 rose off the runway and soared into the clear morning sky. His turret gunner watched the remainder of the A-20s swerve onto the head of the runway from the taxi strip and also roar down the runway before rising into the sky. Capt. Donald Hall, leading the second diamond of A-20s, peered

120

down from his cabin to the jungle below. He knew they would only fly for ten or fifteen minutes before making their attacks. Ioribaiwa was, after all, a mere 32 miles away. Hall would not even have time to meditate on whether or not this new technique would work. He would be over target before he could really settle back in his cabin seat to think about it.

CHAPTER SEVEN

At Ioribaiwa, by 0700 hours, 20 September, Japanese ground troops had just finished breakfast and they were simply loitering in their campsites. The sound of aircraft, however, stiffened the Japanese. Sentinels at their perimeter posts squinted skyward to soon view the shapes to the south, twin engine, single tailed bombers, obviously A-20s. Two of the sentinels wound manual alarms that sent whines screaming throughout the Japanese positions.

Another sentinel ran up to Gen. Tomitaro Horii, who was already awake and had already finished breakfast. "Honorable Horii," the sentinel bowed, "enemy aircraft are approaching, perhaps a dozen of them. May I humbly suggest that you seek shelter."

Horii squinted through the trees for a look,

but he saw nothing.

"They will drop their bombs indiscriminately," the sentinel persisted.

The general nodded, gestured to some aides and then hurried to a shelter.

The Japanese troops had been subjected to irregular air raids all during the pursuit of the Japanese from Kokoda. They were not unduly worried. They knew that from a dozen aircraft only a direct hit on their foxholes could really hurt them. They merely grabbed their gear and headed for foxholes. However most of them merely stood upright in their shelters, squinting through the dense trees for a look at the enemy bombers.

Col. Yosuke Yokoyama scolded some of the soldiers who stood out in the open to gawk up at the sky. "Fools! Do you believe an air raid is a puppet show? Get into your shelters at once!" The soldiers responded.

The troops expected, of course, to hear the whistle of bombs from 2,000 feet or higher from these light bombers and they could cower into their holes before the bombs hit. But suddenly, they lost sight and sound of the aircraft, as though the planes had descended into nowhere beyond their jungle shelters. In fact, the whine of A-20 engines now seemed like some distant echo. Some of the soldiers, uncertain, came out of their shelters for a closer look. Others stopped the sentinels who had come in from the clearing.

"What has happened? Where are the enemy aircraft?"

One of the sentinels shrugged. "They have left the sky, simply dropped from sight. Either they returned to their bases or they have landed on some kunai plain."

Others laughed. The suggestion of landing on some kunai plain beyond their Ioribaiwa perimeter seemed ludicrous.

But then the sound of A-20 engines grew loud and intense. The Japanese soldiers looked at each other, puzzled. What was happening?

The Nankai Shitai Force would soon find out.

Capt. Jim Hennebry brought his planes down to an altitude of 300 feet and then reformed them into single file. Soon they were skimming over the tree tops, occasionally rising over some jungle ridges. Hennebry saw the astonished faces of Japanese sentinels south of the trees, for Hennebry was flying at no more than 200 feet above the ground. Then the captain saw the Japanese soldiers scramble into the trees. As the 90th Squadron leader came closer, he could even see under the trees the clods of earth and ungreen blotches—foxholes and stacks of supplies. The 90th Squadron commander could not believe his eyes—his target right on top of him.

Hennebry dipped his wings, soared over the tree tops and released his frag bombs. The parachutes opened and descended lazily downward. Under the trees and along the trails, the Japanese soldiers stood rigid, gaping, watching the parachutes come down like falling white mushrooms, with small canisters hanging from them. They heard no whistles of bombs, only the roar of planes buzzing the tree tops overhead. A moment later, a staccato of explosions ripped through the foxhole area. Japanese soldiers died, some fell wounded, and stacks of supplies burst into flames.

Before the soldiers recovered, more descending white mushrooms fell into their shelter area, and more staccato explosions ripped up more supplies, killed more soldiers, and wounded more troops. Then, when the next roar came over the trees with still more clusters of descending white parachutes, panic reigned. The Japanese soldiers had not realized what was happening; they only knew that death and destruction came from the white mushrooms. The troops ran in several directions, darting headlong out of their camp areas before the next staccato of explosions sent hot, deadly shrapnel through their campsite.

Almost five thousand men had scattered into the jungles before the last A-20 dropped its parafrag bombs. When the final Havoc was gone, fires roared amidst the stacks of supplies in a dozen areas under the high branches. Trees had been scarred and felled by the small bombs, while dozens of men lay dead with dozens more wounded.

"What happened? What has happened?" Horii asked in astonishment.

A stunned Col. Yosuke Yokoyama only shook his head. "I do not know, Honorable Horii. Never have I experienced anything like this."

Before any of the rattled, confused Japanese soldiers recovered, the roar of planes came again.

This time, .50 caliber strafing fire tore through the trees, igniting more supplies and killing or wounding more men. The tracer fire was deafening, louder than anything the Japanese soldiers had ever heard before. The Japanese did not know that each A-20, from treetop level, was spitting death and destruction from six heavy guns.

Another ten minutes elapsed before the nightmare ended and the sound of A-20 engines diminished to the south. In near total shock, the Japanese troops straggled back to their camps. They ogled at the burning stacks of supplies, the countless potholes from exploding fragmentation bombs, and the scattered dead and wounded. Many hurried to help the injured who writhed in pain or who wiggled frantically along the charred jungle floor.

Col. Yosuke Yokoyama finally brought a parafrag dud to General Horii. "Honorable Commander, here is their new weapon. They are using small parachutes to drop small bombs at almost ground level."

"Impossible," Horii cried. He irritably examined the parafrag, a small parachute with a mere small, 23 pound bomb. "How could they do this? How could they fly so low without striking the trees? Without crashing their aircraft? How?"

"I do not know, Honorable Horii," Yokoyama answered.

"This new strategy was very destructive, and we cannot afford such losses this far from Buna. We must take measures at once to avoid any new attacks of this nature." Horii looked at an aide.

"You will call Captain Saito at once and insist that he keep fighter cover over our positions at all times."

"Yes, General," the aide said, before bowing and scrambling away.

Horii now looked at Yokoyama. "Colonel, we will improvise our 37mm guns as anti aircraft guns, and we will also improvise our .30 caliber machine guns as anti aircraft guns. We will build revetments and keep these weapons in clearings to attack any more such low level enemy aircraft. Should they dare to fly this low again, surely, our guns will easily reach them."

"Yes, General," Colonel Yokoyama said. "I will act at once."

"We must also take other measures," Horii said. "We will no longer keep our troops sheltered in open trenches. We will keep the shelters covered with logs and dirt." He fingered the dud in his hand. "Such a small explosive as this can do nothing over a log and dirt covered shelter."

"I will issue an order at once," Horii's aide said.

"We must not let this surprise today panic us or deter us from our mission. Port Moresby is within our grasp. We have labored and fought too hard to lose this prize now."

As the 12 A-20s landed and rolled to a stop at 3 Mile Drome, the pilots and gunners left their planes like excited children. They literally danced on the wings before leaping to the ground with ecstatic beams on their faces. The ground crews who met then waited anxiously for a report.

"Well, Lieutenant?" a gruff crew chief asked one of the pilots.

"Absolutely unbelievable," the pilot answered. "Right on top of them. We almost flew right down their throats. It was like shooting darts at a board a foot away. We battered their whole campsite; fires all over the place."

"If we had twenty or thirty of those planes on this mission this morning," an A-20 gunner grinned, "we'd have wiped out every goddamn one of those Nip bastards."

"Son of a bitch," the crew chief grinned, "Pappy Gunn did it again."

"He sure did," the gunner grinned once more.

In one of those rare instances during this heartbreaking, struggling, losing war in New Guinea, elation reigned in the canvas quarters of the 3rd Bomb Group's campsite. The chatter was intense, fervent, thrilling. Nobody even complained when somebody said their noon mess would consist of the unappetizing menu of canned bully beef, dehydrated spuds, and dishwater coffee.

The 3rd Bomb Group ground crews in Moresby wasted little time before they were working furiously to clean and reload the A-20 strafing tuns and honeycomb racks. Col. John Davies hoped to send the Havocs out for a second punch at Ioribaiwa this afternoon.

But the Japanese would have something to say about that.

General Tomitaro had done more than order an adjustment in his defenses at Ioribaiwa to temper further parafrag bomb attacks. He also called Buna and spoke angrily to Cmdr. Bunji Shimada of the 4th Kokuta's B Group.

"We were told that the enemy at Port Moresby could no longer mount effective air attacks," Horii raved to the B Group commander. "The Yankee airmen struck this morning with a new type of explosive, small bombs attached to parachutes. They flew over our positions at treetop level height and their attacks were quite devastating.

"Treetop altitude?" Shimada asked in disbelief.

"Treetop!" Horii answered. "They caused serious destruction to our supply dump. It is my belief that if the Americans are allowed to strike us again with this new devil bomb tactic, they may destroy our supplies entirely and we cannot afford such a loss since we are so far from Buna. You must act at once to destroy their airdromes in Port Moresby once and for all."

"You are certain, Honorable Horii, that the aircraft were bombers, and not fighter-bombers as often make an aerial assault from a very low altitude?"

"They were twin engine bombers," General Horii said. "I am told they were the two man A-20 American aircraft."

"Did you recognize any markings on these aircraft, since they came so low?"

"Yes, the aircraft were dark in color, with white bands around the upper portion of the tails."

"Bakarya!" Shimada cursed. "The aircraft were from the contemptuous American 3rd Bomber Sentai. We were certain that Captain Saito's fighter pilots had destroyed them last week when this Yankee air group attempted to attack the resupply convoy to Buna. But the dogs still have aircraft and now they have struck with these new devil tactics as you call them."

"You must destroy their airfield," Horii said again, "for we are ready to begin our drive on Port Moresby."

"We will attack at once," Shimada said. "We will take off from Buna with every available Aichi bomber. I will ask Captain Shingo at Gasmata to make a heavy bomber attack on Moresby this afternoon that will further destroy the runways at Port Moresby." He paused. "When do you expect to begin your assault?"

"We had hoped to resume our offensive tomorrow morning," the Nankai Shitai commander said. "Service troops are at this moment bringing up more supplies from Kokoda and we expect these resources to reach us this afternoon sometime."

"Be assured, Honorable Horii, you will have no more enemy air interference with these new devil tactic aircraft. Our Aichi dive bombers will be over Port Moresby before the morning has ended, and by this afternoon our heavy bombers will complete the destruction of Port Moresby."

"I leave our destiny in your hands, Commander," Horii said.

The B Group commander immediately called

Capt. Uehara Shingo at Gasmata and described this new parachute bomb attack the Americans had launched against Ioribaiwa. Shingo was shocked, for he too was certain Horii would suffer badly if more such air sorties interfered with his offensive.

"When the Honorable Horii described the aircraft that made these attacks," Shimada told Shingo, "I was certain these light bombers came from the brazen 3rd Bomber Sentai. General Horii has requested that we destroy their airdrome as well as their aircraft. I would like permission to launch an Aichi dive bombing attack at once—this morning."

"Yes, yes, of course," Captain Shingo answered. "Call Captain Saito at Lae and arrange fighter plane escort. In the meantime, we will prepare our squadrons of heavy bombers at Gasmata as well as at Arawe for air strikes this afternoon on the Port Moresby airdrome of this 3rd Yankee Sentai."

"Thank you, Captain," Shimada said. "General Horii will be grateful."

Shimada now called Capt. Masahisa Saito at Lae and once more explained the new tactic of the pesky 3rd Bomb Group that had caused consternation at the Nankai Shitai positions in Ioribaiwa. Saito was both puzzled and surprised. He could not quite visualize this new kind of aerial attack with small bombs attached to parachutes. But more important, the Tinian Wing commander also thought that he and his pilots had pretty well finished off the 3rd Bomb Group dur-

131

ing the American attempt to hit the Buna resupply convoy. Saito quickly agreed with Shimada's suggestion to hit Port Moresby with the Aichi dive bombers and the Tinian Wing commander promised to furnish fighter escorts.

"I hope to have our two squadrons of Aichi dive bombers armed and airborne by 0930 hours," Shimada said. "We should reach the usual rendezvous point at the Mambare River bend at 1000 hours. Can I count on a squadron of Mitsubishi fighter planes to join us then?"

"You have my word," Captain Saito answered. "I shall call on Lieutenant Sasai to rendezvous with you at 1000 hours with his squadron of fighter planes."

"Very good," Shimada said.

Lt. Junichi Sasai listened in awe when Captain Saito described the 3rd Bomb Group parafrag assault on Ioribaiwa. The 10 Squadron leader could not quite fathom this new tactic, but the assault had irritated the young squadron leader. Sasai agreed to ready his pilots and aircraft for immediate take off. Within an hour, ground crews at Lae had loaded 24 Zeros of 10 Squadron: Zeros with 20mm shells and full .30 caliber strafing belts. By 0900 hours, the 24 Mitsubishi fighter planes were airborne and droning swiftly to the rendezvous point at the Mambare River bend.

Lieutenant Sasai soon saw the 32 droning Val dive bombers straight ahead and he merely dipped his wings of the lead Zero to acknowledge the sighting, since the Japanese were maintaining their usual radio silence. Captain Shimada then dipped the wing of his own lead Val in response. As soon as the Zeros settled next to the formations of Vals in two hanging columns, Cmdr. Bunji Shimada dropped his lead bomber to just above the peaks of the Owen Stanleys. His Vals and the Zero escorts followed him. As the planes droned on, Shimada saw clear skies ahead and he grinned. He would have good visual and he would not need to come out of the clouds.

At exactly 1030 hours, on this 20 September morning, the air raid sirens wailed across Port Moresby and airmen at the base again hurried from buildings, grass huts, tents, and revetment areas to their foxholes. Soon the whine of Val aircraft, interspersed with the staccato of 40mm and 37mm anti aircraft guns rattled across Port Moresby. Ironically, Col. John Davies had just posted a briefing notice for 1100 hours for the expected afternoon A-20 parafrag strike on Ioribaiwa. Before he asked orderly room personnel to notify squadron commanders, he was forced to seek shelter like everyone else.

Moments later, the first 16 Vals from the 4th Kokutai Wing under Cmdr. Bunji Shingo droned out of the Owen Stanleys and roared toward Koki Airdrome, while the Zeros loitered overhead. Within moments, screaming 200 pound bombs struck 3 Mile Drome with shattering concussions, gouging a series of craters out of the runway and taxiway. Grim Reaper airmen cowered in their shelters, their mouths open, to temper the deafening concussions. Clods of earth spewed upward before descending in cascades of dirt and shrapnel through the mists of dust.

The 35th Fighter Group managed to get a few planes airborne, but the Airacobras were badly outnumbered against 24 superior Zeros and the P-39s failed to interfere with the Japanese bombing run.

The first sweep of Val dive bombers had barely ended when 16 more Val dive bombers roared low and swept over 3 Mile Drome in a second low level bombing and strafing attack. The new assault chopped more holes in the runway and destroyed three A-20s along with two transport planes parked near 3 Mile Drome.

"Jesus," one of the airmen in his foxhole cursed, "they got something personal against us? Every one of those goddamn dive bombers are hitting Koki Drome."

"The bastards are as mad as wet hens," a companion answered. "They must know we're the ones that hit 'em with those parafrags, and the way they're plastering us, we ain't gonna get any of those A-20s up this afternoon for another strike. They've got to knock out that goddamn field at Buna."

"Ah, shit," the first airman said, before he cowered again from a new staccato of exploding bombs. "The heavies and mediums can't hurt Buna because the bastards keep most of their planes under the trees, just like we do. Those A-20s don't pack enough punch. Now, if they had a couple of squadrons of these B-25s that Pappy Gunn's been converting . . ."

"Yeh," the companion said.

The raid on Koki Drome ended some ten minutes after the strikes began. When the last whine of Japanese aircraft faded to the north, airmen came out of their shelters to survey the damage to the runway and taxistrip of 3 Mile Drome. Fortunately, most of the A-20s were under trees and the Japanese had only damaged or destroyed a half dozen of them. Further, the 200 pound bombs could not do quite the damage of 500 pounders. While the Val attack had ruled out any more A-20 parafrag raids today, aviation engineers could probably repair the runway by dark. The A-20s could go out again in the morning to make another parafrag assault on Ioribaiwa.

But Capt. Uehara Shingo had every intention of following up the Val dive bombing attack with heavy 500 pound bomb strikes. The 4th Kokutai commander had acted swiftly. Even as Commander Shimada carried out his attack on 3 Mile Drome in Moresby, Shingo readied 51 Betty bombers, all of the G-M 4 aircraft at the Gasmata airbase on New Britain. He also ordered the two squadrons of Betty bombers at Arawe to prepare for an afternoon air strike. He next called Captain Saito for escort from the Tinian Wing's Zero squadrons at Salamaua for his Gasmata based A Group squadrons. Shingo then decided to call Rabaul and ask for more Zeros that could escort Shingo's other Betty squadrons at Arawe, which he would bring to Gasmata to prepare for afternoon heavy bomber strikes on Moresby. Thus, with about a hundred Bettys, Shingo could truly put a dent in the Port Moresby airfields.

When Shinga made his request for extra Zeros, Adm. Junichi Kasaka balked. "You must understand, Captain, that we are heavily engaged with the enemy in the Solomons at this time. We need every Mitsubishi fighter plane available here in Rabaul."

"But think of our position in New Guinea, Honorable Kasaka," Captain Shingo answered. "The American bombers in Port Moresby have attacked the Nankai Shitai positions at Ioribaiwa with a new tactic, dropping small bombs attached to parachutes. With this new technique, they were able to drop their explosives from treetop level and thus cause considerable damage to our ground positions. Fortunately, they only sent a few aircraft. But should they make such attacks with massive formations of aircraft, they could utterly destroy General Horii's positions and end his hopes for advancing on Port Moresby."

"This is a distressing thought," Kasaka admitted.

"It is my understanding that the enemy in Port Moresby fully expects General Horii to attack," Captain Shingo continued. "I believe this new aerial tactic is a desperate measure. Surely, we must not give our enemies any respite."

"No, of course not," Kusaka wavered.

"Already this morning, Commander Shimada is conducting an aerial assault on Port Moresby with his Aichi dive bombers. Hopefully, he will knock out the Koki Airdrome which we are certain houses the aircraft of the pesky 3rd Bomber

Sentai. I believe we must knock out all of the enemy's fighter plane and bomber plane airdromes as the enemy may arm other light aircraft with these same parachute bombs. Only another heavy strike, such as the one we launched in August, can assure the destruction of these airfields. In fact, I would like to make this an even bigger strike, using all four squadrons of our G-M 4 heavy bombers of the 4th Kokutai."

"I see the logic of your thinking, Captain."

"I intend to fly two squadrons of heavy bombers to Buna this afternoon for a strike on Port Moresby late today or at first light tomorrow. I would also like to make a second strike with two G-M 4 squadrons at Arawe, which will stage from Gasmata. However, I do not believe that Captain Saito has enough Mitsubishi fighter planes in Lae and Salamaua to escort all the bombers of the 4th Kokutai Wing. I therefore need at least another squadron of fighter planes to carry out these massive strikes."

"Perhaps I can spare a squadron," Admiral Kasaka said.

"Could you send to Gasmata the 11 Squadron of Lt. Cmdr. Tadashi Nakajima? He and his pilots have flown many sorties out of Lae, and they are quite familiar with the Papuan terrain, and with our operations in New Guinea."

"11 Squadron has been conducting sorties in the Solomons and perhaps a change will do them good. All right, I will ask Lieutenant Commander Nakajima to fly his squadron at once to Gasmata. But, Captain, once you have completed the task of destroying the American airfields at Port Moresby, I would ask that you send Nakajima's squadron back to Rabaul at once. The conflict in the Solomons is quite intense and we need every resource."

"Thank you, Honorable Kasaka," Captain Shingo said. "Not only I, but General Horii too will be eternally grateful for your consideration."

"We must do what we must," Kasaka said. "And Captain, good luck. May the Gods of our Samurai ancestors favor your endeavor."

"I thank you for your prayers and help, Admiral."

Thus, Capt. Uehara Shingo got what he needed for a replay of the 11 August aerial assault on Port Moresby—only this time he would have many more aircraft. He was quite confident he would succeed. After talking to the 24th Air Flotilla commander, he completed arrangements for twin heavy bomber strikes against Moresby for either this afternoon or tomorrow. He would use four Squadrons of Bettys this time, nearly a hundred heavy bombers. He would also call for more strikes by the Val dive bombers. Shingo was satisfied. This would be the largest formation of bombers ever sent against a target during the Papuan campaign.

CHAPTER EIGHT

At 1045 hours, after the Val dive bombing raid, Col. John Davies stood at the end of 4 Mile Drome with Maj. Bob Strickland and other officers of the 3rd Bomb Group. Also with Davies was Maj. Paul Pappy Gunn. The officers stared at the small potholes on the runway and then squinted at the curling smoke of the three burning A-20s that the Japanese dive bombers had set afire and destroyed.

"You know something, Johnny," Maj. Bob Strickland said, "those sons of bitches were after us this time; only us and nobody else."

"What the hell did you expect?" Gunn grinned. "You're the guys that worked them over at Ioribaiwa this morning. They were incensed so you must have done a good job."

"Well, we can't use this runway for any low

level A-20 strike this afternoon, that's for sure," Strickland said.

One of the other officers turned to Pappy Gunn. "Pappy, do you think they'll get this strip back in condition by tomorrow?"

"Hell, with the kind of equipment Lou Sverdrup and his 808th Aviation Engineers have now, they can have this runway patched up in a couple of hours," Pappy Gunn said. "Now if they hit us with their heavies, that would be something else. But even then, Sverdrup could have us back in shape within a day." Gunn squinted up at the sky. "Those Nips don't understand. They might need a week to get a strip back in shape if we mauled them with something heavy, and they still think we operate with shovels and wheelbarrows. Yes sir," Gunn nodded, almost to himself. "If we could do in their runways like they did us, they'd be in trouble."

"If we could only knock out that goddamn Buna and maybe Gasmata," John Davies scowled. "That'd stop those Bettys and Vals for a while."

"We'd need B-25s like the ones Major Gunn converted," one of the officers said. "That'd sure do the job on them."

Paul Pappy Gunn pursed his lips, stroked his round chin, and he suddenly grinned at John Davies. "I know where you can find a couple dozen B-25s. We've gained a lot of experience working on the Mitchells at Townsville; we could convert a couple dozen B-25s in maybe two days."

John Davies frowned. "Where the hell are there

two dozen B-25s?"

"Brisbane," Paul Gunn said. "There are twenty four new spanking B-25s sitting on Archer Field in Brisbane. If we can get them back here by tonight, I could have at least half of them converted by sometime tomorrow. You could make your low level strike on Buna."

Strickland and Davies exchanged puzzled looks.

"Of course, I'd need a couple hundred fifty caliber guns," Gunn said, "but we'd have to stop at Townsville anyway to refuel. I know Major Benson there of the 4th Air Depot and he owes me a favor."

"Pappy, are you talking sense?" Davies asked.

"They said the 3rd Group planes were on the way," Pappy Gunn shrugged. "How do you know those aren't your Mitchells down there in Brisbane?" He leaned closer to the 3rd Group commander. "Go see the old man. Tell him I said your planes are down in Archer Field and you'd like to go down and get them. Ask him for an authorization."

"You're crazy, Pappy," Davies said.

"You want to knock out Buna, don't you?" Gunn said. "Go see the old man."

John Davies grinned and within a half hour he arrived at 5th Air Force ADVON headquarters at the old Port Moresby Hotel to see General Whitehead. The old man grinned when he saw Davies and he pumped the hand of the 3rd Group commander. "That was a hell of a job this morning, Johnny, a hell of a job."

"We were going out again this afternoon, but those Japanese bombers took care of that."

Whitehead rubbed his bent nose. "The bastards. If we could knock out Buna or if we could knock out Lae—without escorts, Wagner and Lynch and Jackson could make short work of those Bettys and Vals."

Davies leaned over the general's desk. "We can knock out Lae and Buna if we had enough B-25 attack bombers. A couple dozen low level Mitchells, dumping maybe a thousand parafrags and ten fifties in the nose—they'd take care of Buna."

Whitehead frowned.

"Ennis," Davies said, "Pappy Gunn tells me our B-25s are in Brisbane. Give me an authorization. Pappy and I will take a plane load of pilots down there to pick them up. Gunn says if we have them back tonight, he can have at least half of them converted by sometime tomorrow. We'll take care of Buna."

Now Whitehead scowled. "Did Pappy Gunn put you up to this? That thieving, conniving maverick? You know goddamn well you don't have any B-25s in Brisbane. If there's any Mitchells at Archer Field, we don't own them."

"The 3rd Group planes were on the way," Davies said, "Washington said they were. You wouldn't be doing anything wrong if you gave me permission to go down to Australia to pick up *my* planes. Nobody could fault you if we picked up the wrong aircraft; if we mistook those B-25s for the ones Washington promised. We're the only group in the Southwest Pacific using B-25s."

Whitehead meditated for a moment. "I got a suspicion those Mitchells belong to the Dutch, but the bastards may never use them."

"How about the authorization, Ennis?"

"You're crazy, Johnny," Whitehead shook his head. "They're going to get Pappy one of these days; you can bet on it. He steals, connives, manipulates, and I don't know what all else. Now he wants to steal aircraft. He'll get your ass in a sling if you go along with him. Anyway, where the hell will you get a couple hundred guns to convert those B-25s."

"In Townsville. Pappy says he knows the air depot commander there."

"That figures," Whitehead scowled again.

"Ennis, I'd rather have my ass in a sling than a grave in Port Moresby."

"You'll be sitting at the same court-martial with Gunn."

"How about three of us sitting in at that court-martial?" Davies said. He leaned closer to the general. "Once those planes are back in New Guinea and Pappy modifies them, those bastards won't stage out of Buna anymore, I guarantee it."

"This is not by the book, Johnny."

"Since when did we go by the book up here in Moresby?"

"Okay," Whitehead sighed, rubbing his bent nose again. "I'll give you an authorization to pick up *your* planes."

After the 3rd Group commander got the general's authorization, he returned immediately to the 3rd Group campsite and found Pappy Gunn.

143

Major Gunn greeted Davies warmly. "You sold him," he said, his eyes brightening. "I knew you would. The Old Man's got a war to fight up here; he can't worry about regulations." Then he cocked his head. "The mail plane will be leaving for Brisbane about 1300 hours. Maybe we can be on it."

Davies nodded and then found Major Strickland. "Get twenty-four pilots ready on the double for a ride to Brisbane."

"We're really going after those B-25s, huh?" Strickland grinned. "I know one goddamn thing. We can do an awful lot with twenty-four new Mitchells. They may have my ass along with yours, Johnny, but I know I'd have been buried up here a long time ago if it weren't for those Aussies in the Owen Stanleys. I owe them something."

"I'm going over to the 808th Engineers," Davies said. "Have those pilots ready by the time I get back."

Colonel Davies now called on Col. Louis Sverdrup of the 808th Aviation Engineer Battalion, that was responsible for the repair and upkeep of airdromes, dispersal areas, and runways. The 808th had been quite busy with clean up and repair at Moresby because of frequent Japanese air raids. Davies found Sverdrup where expected — directing the repair of 3 Mile Drome.

Colonel Sverdrup expressed astonishment when Davies made his request: 24 dispersal revetments under the cover of dense trees for 24 Mitchells, with the dispersal areas at considerable distance from the taxistrip. Further, Davies wanted all other work suspended so that every available man and piece of equipment could be used on this priority project. The revetments must be completed by tomorrow morning. If need be, the engineers should work all night.

"That's impossiblle, Johnny," Sverdrup said. "I don't know if I got enough men and equipment to do that by tomorrow morning."

Davies showed Sverdrup Whitehead's authorization. Sverdrup looked at the authorization and then shrugged. It made sense. After all, the 3rd had been promised new planes for weeks. "Okay, Johnny, we'll get on it as soon as we patch up the runways."

At 1300 hours, 23 pilots, along with Major Strickland, Major Gunn, and Colonel Davies stood waiting on 7 Mile Drome while a C-47 crew unloaded mail and other supplies from the transport plane. While tankmen with tank trucks refueled the plane, Davies and his pilots climbed aboard. When the pilot and copilot of the transport plane returned to their aircraft, they were astonished to see the aircraft loaded with passengers.

"Colonel," the pilot said to Davies, "what the hell's going on?"

"We're going back to Brisbane with you," Davies said, "to pick up our B-25s." He showed the pilot his authorization from General Whitehead.

"Okay," the transport pilot shrugged. "We'll be making a stop at Chartres Towers to refuel before we go on to Brisbane. We should be at Archer Field at about 1700 hours late this afternoon."

The C-47 took off for the 900 mile trip to Brisbane and stopped briefly 600 miles later at Chartres Towers in northern Australia to refuel. Then the transport plane continued on. By 1700 hours, the control tower operator at Archer Field gave landing instructions to the transport pilot, who had arrived right on time after the long flight from New Guinea. Most of the 3rd Group pilots had slept during the long flight for they would be flying during much of the evening.

Nonchalantly, brusquely, and with routine authority, Col. John Davies presented his authorization to the American OD officer at Archer Field. The duty captain, like others around the base, knew little of high level staff activities concerning allotments, strategies, and operations.

"I wondered who the hell owned these planes," the captain said. "Jesus, they've been sitting here for weeks."

The captain did not question the authorization. In fact, the OD officer called the ordnance NCO to check out the fuel supply in the Mitchells before he called the control tower to prepare for takeoff.

After a hot meal and hot coffee at Archer Field, Col. John Davies, his pilots, and Maj. Paul Gunn shuffled toward the pre-flighting B-25s. At 1830 hours, as the sun began settling below the Brisbane River, the B-25s taxied in single file to the end of the runway. On signal from the tower, the Mitchells, one by one, rose into the northern sky. By 1900 hours, the last Mitchell had left Brisbane and was droning northward.

Not until 2100 hours did military authorities in Brisbane learn that an air corps colonel and a group of pilots had taken off with the new B-25s. The OD officer had merely talked about it in casual conversation with base officers during an evening coffee break. Two staff officers, who knew the B-25s had been consigned to the Dutch, listened in shock. Within a half hour the staff officers were frantically trying to determine how the colonel had gotten an authorization to pick up the planes. They phoned SWPA bases up and down the east coast of Australia, dragging some officers away from dinner or club parties. By the time 5th Air Force aides in Brisbane called Townsville, among other places, Davies had stopped there to refuel and loaded aboard some of the B-25s some 200 .50 caliber guns that Pappy Gunn had somehow wheedled out of the 4th Air Depot.

John Davies had also called 3rd Bomb Group headquarters in Moresby and spoken to the group executive officer. He told him the planes would be in Moresby at about 2400 hours and the executive officer should have ground crews waiting to direct them off the runways. He also asked the executive officer to check with 808th Engineers and to make sure they had the dispersal areas ready by daylight.

However, before the 3rd Group airmen boarded the B-25s and flew off, the Townsville base commander and a squad of helmeted

MPs sped in two jeeps toward Colonel Davies and his pilots.

"Colonel, sir," the major said, "I have orders from 5th Air Force to hold these B-25s at Townsville. They say your authorization is invalid. Nobody can reach General Whitehead to verify your orders."

"Major," Colonel Davies said, "I've got a written authorization and you've got an oral one. You must understand that under Army Regulations a signed order supersedes an oral one. We were told that our B-25s were in Brisbane and I merely brought my 3rd Group pilots here to pick them up. We found the B-25s at Archer Field and we simply flew off with them."

"The colonel's authorization is valid," Pappy Gunn now spoke. "I had a proper authorization to pick up strafing guns, too. You can check with Major Benson at the 4th Air Depot."

The base major rolled his tongue around his lips.

Davies suddenly sobered. "We need those planes bad, Major."

The Townsville base commander looked at the loitering 3rd Group pilots, a mixture of apprehension and supplication on the faces of the pilots. Technically, Colonel Davies and Major Gunn were correct. Written orders did take precedence over oral orders.

The major then squinted at the B-25s on the field, their fuselages rocking from warming engines—like anxious hounds ready to pursue game. The base commander knew well enough the desperate struggle in New Guinea, 500 miles away across the Coral Sea. He remembered vividly when 22nd Bomb Group and 19th Bomb Group bombers were based here, when they regularly flew up to stage out of Moresby to attack the Japanese; and he remembered most that so many of the B-26s and the B-17s had failed to return to Townsville. And the major had heard of the successful A-20 strike this morning at Ioribaiwa that had given a respite to the Australian Diggers at Imita. He knew that Pappy Gunn had carried out miraculous aircraft salvage work right here in Townsville. If these B-25s could stem the Japanese tide in New Guinea, who was this major to deny big John Davies and Paul Pappy Gunn the opportunity to do so?

The major looked first at Gunn and then at Col. John Davies. "Is Crazy Pappy going to modify these planes too?"

"Just as soon as we get back to New Guinea," Davies said. "Then we're going to hit Buna."

"You're going to have twenty-four Pappy Follies, huh?" the major grinned. Then, the Townsville base commander sighed. "I guess you're right, Colonel, a written order does supersede an oral one." He shook his head. "I'd love to see the faces on those bastards when you go over Buna."

"Thanks, Major," Davies said.

"Sure," the major nodded. Then, he cocked his head toward the MPs who simply dispersed.

While the major was on the field watching the 3rd Group pilots board their B-25s, he had received two phone calls from Brisbane. Aides rushed out to the field to tell him. Brisbane wanted to know, the aides said, if the major had held up the B-25s here in Townsville. Had he confined the brazen 3rd Group colonel and his pilots? He informed his aides to tell Brisbane he was looking into the matter because Col. John Davies had a signed authorization from 5th Air Force ADVON headquarters in Port Moresby.

"At the moment," the major said, looking at the B-25s, "you can call back Brisbane and tell them the planes are still here."

"Yes sir," the aide answered.

At 2100 hours, the Townsville base commander stood in the field control tower and watched the B-25s take off. After the last B-25 had disappeared into the dark skies over the Coral Sea, the major returned to his office where he found an urgent request to call Brisbane, regardless of the hour. Somewhat nervous, the Townsville base commander called Brisbane. This time, an aide to General Kenney himself spoke with the major. Had the major carried out instructions? Too late. The planes had already taken off.

"What? You let them take off with those planes?"

"I'm sorry, sir," the major told Kenney's aide. "Colonel Davies had a written authorization and he left here before I could determine whether or not the authorization was valid."

"You idiot!" the aide cried. "I'll have your ass for this!"

"Yes sir."

At 2400 hours, while a deep midnight darkness hung over Port Moresby, the drone of planes prompted men at 3 Mile Drome to rush out to the airstrip to ignite runway oil drum lights. Swiftly, the B-25s touched down on the repaired 3 Mile runway. When they taxied to the far end of the strip, men in waiting jeeps motioned to the pilots to follow them over the rough field to prepared hiding places in the jungle. The 808th Engineers had done its job well and they had completed the revetments under trees. By 0100 hours, the Mitchells had been safely tucked away and the oil fires along the runway snuffed out.

Third Bomb Group crews hugged their B-25s and patted the newly painted olive green surfaces affectionately. They were awed by these new planes, aircraft that did not need patches for fuselages or tails or wings; aircraft that did not need new engines or new electrical systems, and new armament equipment. The ground crews did not rest long, for Mad Professor Gunn soon put every available man to work in converting the B-25s into low level attack bombers.

At 0630 AM, while Gunn and his men still worked on the Mitchells, Japanese bombers came over Port Moresby. Once more their whistling bombs potholed 3 Mile Drome. Once more some aircraft went up in smoke: two A20s, three P-40s, and two P-39s, along with a couple of C-47 transports. And again, before the 35th and 8th American fighter planes or the 75 Squadron Australian fighter planes could rise to pursue the interlopers, the bombers and their Zero escorts had vanished over the Owen Stanley Mountains.

"The bastards," Col. John Davies complained.

"Don't complain," Pappy Gunn said. "They never touched one of those new B-25s. The 808th will have that strip back in shape by noon and I'll have sixteen converted Mitchells ready to go."

"Okay," John Davies said, "I trust you."

In Australia, at this same 0630 hours, the understanding major at Townsville was already confined to quarters to await court martial. The major's neglect had allowed an air force colonel to abscond with 24 new aircraft without a true authorization. The neglect of duty was intolerable. When the Dutch heard the news they were infuriated. This was the second time the Americans had pilfered Dutch consigned items. The Americans had stolen those bombsights and now they had gone too far to brazenly steal their planes. They demanded from SWPA headquarters that the Mitchells be returned at once to Brisbane or they would go to the U. S. State Department.

Almost at once, brass in Brisbane, Australia, sent frantic radio messages to Port Moresby, New Guinea: "Return 24 B-25s at once to Brisbane." However, 5th Air Force ADVON personnel pleaded ignorance. They knew nothing of any unauthorized aircraft in Moresby. Brisbane would need to speak to General Whitehead, and he was "somewhere out in the field." The SWPA brass could only tell the Dutch that 5th Air Force would send a board of inquiry to Port Moresby to look into the matter.

Of course, there was little chance of such an inquiry board reaching Moresby very soon, for none of the brass wallowing in Brisbane luxury was prepared to fly personally to Moresby's steaming jungles to take a personal hand.

About noon, somebody in Brisbane did finally reach General Whitehead. Why had the ADVON commander authorized Col. John Davies to pick up the aircraft that had been consigned to the Dutch? Whitehead pleaded the same ignorance as his staff. He had merely allowed the colonel to pick up B-25s that had been promised from Washington. Apparently, Davies had picked up the wrong planes.

The aide grumbled, lost for words, but moments later, General Kenney himself was on the phone. "Ennis, we could have an international incident on our hands over this thing. The Dutch are furious and they threaten to go to the State Department. You'll have to get those B-25s back to Australia."

"I can't do that," Whitehead said.

"What the hell do you mean, you can't?" Kenney barked.

"The Nips have hit our runways for two days running," Whitehead said, "and we're trying to repair them. If we take those B-25s out in the open, Bettys could destroy them on the ground. We've got to take out their staging area in Buna before we bring those Mitchells into the open. The Dutch wouldn't want a bunch of wrecked B-25s, would they?"

"Buna!" Kenney cried. "The only way to take

out Buna is maybe with converted low level medium bombers like the ones Pappy Gunn was working on up there." Kenney paused and then gasped. "Goddamn it, Ennis, you didn't turn those B-25s over to that Mad Professor, did you? Is he converting those Mitchells to low level attack bombers to hit Buna?"

Bent Nose Whitehead did not answer.

"Ennis, you've got to do the right thing here."

"Where those B-25s are concerned, George," Whitehead said, "you can be sure I'll do the right thing."

Gen. George Kenney clearly understood the implication in Whitehead's answer, but the 5th Air Force commander, in good conscience, could not argue with Whitehead's inference. In fact, Kenney himself saw in his mind the image of utter surprise on the faces of Japanese when B-25s came roaring over the Buna airfield at tree top level. The 5th Air Force commander would merely make promises to anybody who pressured him. They would get the unauthorized B-25s back to Brisbane as soon as they could. Kenney only hoped MacArthur would agree with him. True, MacArthur had told Kenney the air show was his. But would MacArthur include in this free hand the right to create an international incident?

CHAPTER NINE

The morning of 22 September broke dark and dreary for the remnants of intermittent rain during the night had left low, dark clouds hanging over New Guinea. A thick cover had completely closed in Papua. A Yak tableland low had moved into the Bismarck Archipelago on the afternoon of 20 September, forestalling Captain Shingo's plan to attack Port Moresby with his Betty bombers. All during the day of 21 September, the dense, low clouds had continued, with heavy rains drenching New Guinea throughout the period. And by this 22 September morning, visibility was still under a thousand feet, and Shingo's bombers were still grounded. The 4th Kokutai Wing commander had moved the Bettys of his A group into Buna and he had moved his other Bettys from Arawe and the Zeros from Rabaul into Gasmata. The aircraft had been sitting idle for more that 36 hours, waiting for a break in the weather.

For the Allies the same delays also prevailed. The latest meteorological reports at 5th Air Force ADVON headquarters in Moresby indicated that the poor weather would linger over New Guinea for perhaps another two days. When this weather report reached ADVON at 0500, the operations staff called all OD officers of the various air units to once more cancel all planned missions until further notice.

Many of the men at the 3rd Bomb Group had been up early, mostly from curiosity. Supply clerks, radio men, orderly room clerks, and even squadron medics were anxious to see the altered B-25s. They funnelled to the area under the trees beyond 3 Mile Drome where Pappy Gunn and his engineering crews had been working furiously for 36 hours. Here, the spectators watched the heavy hammering, acetelyne torch cutting, and the heavy welding as men cut away bombardier compartments from aircraft before installing six heavy .50 caliber strafing guns in the nose and welding four more such guns to the fuselages.

The men of the 3rd Bomb Group had been quite skeptical of the honeycomb racks and six big guns jutting out of the noses of the A-20s, but the surprising success with these A-20s had convinced them such adaptations had been worthwhile. Now, the early risers stared just as curiously at the medium bomber adaptations. Pappy Gunn and his mechanics had just completed their work on sixteen of the B-25s, the work taking much longer than predicted. Fortunately bad weather, grounding aircraft from both sides, had given Gunn and his crews time to complete the job.

"Jesus," a supply clerk said to a companion, "will those planes really get off the ground with all that hardware in front?"

"I know one thing," his companion shook his head, "I wouldn't fly in one of those goddamn things."

The two supply clerks moved closer to a B-25 and one of them touched a gun welded to the fuselage. "It's on there tight enough, so I guess it won't fall off."

"It won't fall off," a burly engineering sergeant suddenly grinned at the two supply clerks. "By the time we've got full daylight, we'll have sixteen of these babies ready for the bastards."

One of the clerks squinted up at the gray, low hanging clouds. "Maybe, but you're not going anywhere with those Mitchells today anymore than you could yesterday. Christ, you can't even see Mount Imita."

"Maybe not," the engineering officer said, "but these converted Mitchells don't need any altitude. They can attack at treetop level, so all they need is maybe a two or three hundred feet ceiling."

"Sure," one of the clerks scoffed, "and how the hell do they get over the Owen Stanleys in weather like this?"

"Instruments," the sergeant said, "they use their instruments."

"Ah, that's a crock 'a shit," the clerk gestured disdainfully. "I'll admit, those A-20s did all right at Ioribaiwa, but I can't believe these Mitchells can do the same thing; not with those ten big guns up front."

"Just stick around kid," the sergeant said, "and you'll see it."

The two supply clerks then ignored the engineering sergeant and, with other curious 3rd Group ground personnel, they continued to watch welders and ordnance men work on another B-25.

At another Mitchell, Col. John Davies and Maj. Bob Strickland stood next to Maj. Gunn and watched the ordnance men fit a final gun on the fuselage of the B-25. The sergeant then turned to Gunn and grinned.

"Okay, Major, sixteen of them are finished."

Major Gunn nodded and then looked at Davies. "Well, Johnny, counting the four we converted earlier, you've got twenty of them ready to go. It took longer than I expected, but they're ready."

Major Bob Strickland looked up at the low clouds. "Too bad we can't go out today, Johnny."

"Why can't you go out today?" Pappy Gunn asked. "These converted planes are designed to work at treetop level. All you need is a few hundred feet ceiling, same as the A-20s. Hell, you could catch those Nips with total surprise."

John Davies looked up at the dense clouds, rubbed his chin, and then looked at Gunn. "Pappy, do you really think so? There's a lot of goddamn mountain peaks between here and Buna."

Pappy Gunn grinned. "Johnny, we've checked the altimeters thoroughly in every one of these planes, and you've got contour maps of Papua. Don't forget, once you clear the mountains, you've got maybe thirty miles of kunai plains before you reach the Buna airfield. Hell, you could come over that airfield like a grasscutter."

"Goddamn it, Pappy," John Davies grinned, "you convinced me. Are you sure the B-25s are ready to go?"

"Never more certain."

"Okay," Davies nodded, "I'm going over to see old man Whitehead. Jesus, we could really do a job on them today. Not only can we surprise them, but we'd shock hell out of them with these B-25s dropping parafrags and spitting tracers from ten big guns from treetop level."

"You'll never get a better chance to catch them napping."

Meanwhile, at this same 0530 hours, a curiosity prevailed among the Australian ground personnel of 22 Squadron, five miles away at 4 Mile Drome. Australian engineering crews had fitted honeycomb racks on half of the squadron's Beauforts since yesterday morning—on orders from 5th Air Force ADVON. Now the twin engine light bombers took on a strange appearance. Aussies meandered about the revetment area, peering curiously at the strange contraptions under the wings. These ground crews had vaguely heard that 22 Squadron pilots had been practicing on some new low level bombing technique, but they had paid little attention to the reports. Now, they guessed that the strange honeycomb racks under the Beaufort wings had something to do with these practice sessions.

"Damn," a lance corporal said to a companion, "that's the looniest thing I ever saw."

"After that 'it a couple days ago by the 3 Bomb, Old Man White'ead made Cap'ain Lukis put the same bloody racks on 'alf our aircraft. I guess the general intends to use this new parachute bomb on most 'a the light planes we 'ave 'ere in Moresby."

"They worked, did they?" the first man asked.

"You know what 'appened after 3 Bomb 'it those bloody Nips at Kokoda, don't you? The Nips 'it 3 Bomb's drome with a vengeance. That should answer you."

"But can our Aussie flyers do it?"

"We been wonderin' what kind of practice they were on," the corporal said. "Now we know, don't we? I guess the order came from Kenney 'imself, it did. Some of the pilots don't like it; don't like it at all."

"Still, if the tactic works like they say it did for the 3 Bomb, this parachute bomb may be just the thing we need to turn around this bloody air war."

The lance corporal nodded and then peered up at the gloomy, low hanging clouds that held fast over Port Moresby. "I 'eard our boys were supposed to try out those new tactics today, but it don't look like it, not in this kind 'a weather."

"No," the companion nodded.

In the 4 Mile Drome mess, A/C Frank Lukis and other pilots of 22 Squadron ate breakfast along with Lt. Larry Jackson and some of his fighter pilots of 75 Squadron. The RAAF flyers had been up early because they had fully expected to fly a morning mission, possibly over Ioribaiwa with these new parafrag bombs. They had been still asleep at 0500 when the order came from ADVON on cancellations of all missions. Since they had not been informed, they had arisen early. Now they ate toast, scrambled powdered eggs, a small portion of canned prunes in between sips of tea. When Jackson finished a mouthful of food, he turned to Commander Lukis.

"Frank, is there any chance we may still go out today?"

"Not according to 5th ADVON," Lukis said. "They say these 'eavy clouds will 'ang about for another day, at least."

"Too bad," Jackson answered. "I'd 'ave loved to see what kind of job you and your lads could do with those new parachute bombs. Did your engineering lads finish putting those racks on your Beaus?"

"About 'alf of them," Lukis said,

Then, Larry Jackson suddenly grinned. "You think your lads 'ave 'ad enough practice on this new technique?"

"Two hours, we 'ad, that's all," one of the 22 Squadron pilots said. "I'll say one thing: it was eerie, it was — watching a glob of small parachutes fall off your wings like floating mushrooms. But we got so close to the ground, we couldn't miss the target."

Larry Jackson shook his head. "Damn, if Kenney intends to 'ave everybody in Moresby use those things, where the 'ell is 'e getting them?"

"I 'eard that Kenney 'as a whole warehouse full of those bombs and 'e's been sending them up 'ere to Moresby as fast as 'e can load them on Dakota transport planes."

"We need big ones, two hundred and five hundred pounders," another of the 22 Squadron pilots gestured between mouthfuls of food. "I don't think those little firecrackers can really 'urt the Nips, no matter 'ow many of those dusters we carry under wings."

"Well," another Beaufort pilot said, "Kenney's the chief and we do as 'e says." He looked at Frank Lukis. "That's right, sir, isn't it?"

"Don't get upset, lads," Lukis said. "We'll need to give these new parachute bombs a try. When you consider 'ow the bloody Nips 'ave 'ad everything their way in this damn war, what've we got to lose?"

Other pilots at the breakfast table nodded.

Lukis, a dark, husky, energetic man, had been in the RAAF since the mid-30s, and he had now attained the rank of air commander. He had fought out of Darwin against the Japanese and he had then worked with Northeast Australia Defense Command before taking over 22 Squadron while the unit trained in Australia. Lukis had been one of the few Australians who had gotten on well with General Brett, who had called Lukis

162

a very helpful and cooperative person when Brett was trying to organize the Far East Air Forces. Lukis had both a keen mind and a sharp sense of humor.

Lukis had been amazed when the 9th RAAF Group commander had diverted his 22 Squadron from the Buna mission to hit barges off Salamaua. He had complained, but he still did as his group commander ordered. But Lukis had also expected the consequences, the dismissal of the 9th's commander, for he suspected that Whitehead would never tolerate such disdainful independent action. While others had complained of the dismissal, Lukis had reminded his fellow Australian airmen that only complete cooperation could change around the air war in Papua.

Lukis understood Kenney's problem of trying to hit airfield targets with light bombers and he had been one of the few Australians who did not balk at the use of the parafrag bomb tactic.

Now Lukis turned to Lieutenant Jackson. "Larry, I 'ope you lads are sharp. If we use these new parachute bombs and they're as nasty as these 3 Bomb airmen say they are, the Nips will 'it back like angry wasps. Your fighter pilots will need to be alert and aggressive."

Lt. Larry Jackson grinned. "Aren't we always on our toes?"

Frank Lukis nodded. The 22 Squadron air commander liked Jackson for the young squadron leader had never faltered, regardless of the usually heavy odds from Zero interceptors. Jackson had been a pilot with 75 Squadron back when the squadron was under the command of Jackson's own brother, who had been killed in action in May. By June, the battered 75 Squadron had returned to Australia for rest and retraining. In Australia, Larry Jackson won command of the squadron and was glad to get back to New Guinea after the Japanese landed at Buna. He wanted a new crack at the Japanese, especially since the Japanese had killed his brother.

Five miles to the southwest, at the very edge of the jungles in the sprawling Port Moresby airbase, was 7 Mile Drome, with its 6,000 feet runway, the longest at Moresby. The dozens of revetments surrounding the runway might as likely be empty of aircraft as filled. 7 Mile Drome, near the native village of Waigani, was a staging drome for the big planes that came up from Australia, the B-26s of the 22nd Group and the B-17s of the 43rd and 90th Groups.

The bigger aircraft remained permanently based in northern Australia on an airfield at the tip of the Cape Horn Peninsula. Only when Whitehead called for long range strikes on Gasmata or Rabaul did the B-26s and B-17s come to Moresby. They merely loaded and gassed up here before flying to New Britain targets. When they returned from a bombing mission, the Marauders and Fortresses merely refueled and then flew back to their Australian bases.

Gen. George Kenney and Gen. Ennis Whitehead had a great fear for the heavy bombers. They knew the Japanese loved to destroy big planes on the ground much more than destroying fighter planes or light bombers. And with the frequent Japanese air assaults on Moresby, both Kenney and Whitehead frowned on keeping heavy bombers permanently based here. Further, while Washington sometimes answered 5th Air Force pleas for more planes with P-39s, A-20s, and sometimes B-25s, they rarely sent replacement B-26 and B-17 aircraft.

However, on this gloomy 22 September morning, the 7 Mile Drome revetment areas were jammed with planes. Some 24 B-26s of the 22nd Bomb Group and 12 B-17s of the 43rd Bomb Group sat in the nooks about the long runway. The Marauders and Fortresses had come into Moresby on the afternoon of 20 September to make strikes on Gasmata and Rabaul the next morning—just as Shingo's Betty bombers had come into Buna on the same afternoon to make strikes on Moresby the next day. But the Yak low pressure system had kept these bigger bombers grounded for more than 36 hours—just as the weather front had kept Shingo's heavy bombers grounded in Buna and Gasmata. So here at 7 Mile Drome in Moresby the B-26s and B-17s sat, waiting for who knew what.

At 0545 hours, Col. Dwight Devine, commander of the 22nd Bomb Group, left the 7 Mile Drome mess hall and now walked leisurely toward the long runway. Two of his bomber pilots walked alongside of him.

"Well, Colonel?" one of them asked.

Devine squinted up at the low clouds and scowled. "Shit, we can't go anyplace today, either.

165

And I heard the 19th was coming up this morning with a dozen B-17s."

"Goddamn it, Colonel," the pilot said, "that's all we need, fifty bombers jammed at this airfield. If the weather breaks before we get out of here, the Japanese might do an awful job. Those bastards love to hit heavies. And from what I hear, they've really got their balls in an uproar after that A-20 parafrag strike."

"I know," Devine nodded.

"They've only been able to come over the mountains with light bombers for the last couple of days because of the weather, and not many at that. They must be itching to hit Moresby again with their heavies. I bet they've got a horde of Bettys ready at Gasmata and maybe even in Buna."

"Would I like to catch a couple hundred heavies on the ground at someplace like Buna," Dwight Devine grinned.

"Well, Colonel," the first officer said, "you're not going to catch any in this kind of weather."

"I guess not," the 22nd Group commander answered.

Dwight Devine had been a veteran pilot of the old 17th Bomb Group in the Philippines. Like big John Davies, Devine had also suffered through the aggravating defeats in the Philippines, Java, and Timor. He had been in Brisbane, without assignment, when the 22nd Group arrived in Australia with their 50 crated B-26s. General Brett had asked Devine to assume command of this new group, and Devine had rounded up some of his old experienced bomber pilots, men like Capt. Walter Greer, Capt. Walter Krell, or Maj. Pat O'Donnell to train the newcomers and weld the new group into an efficient air unit.

Devine's 22nd had taken its share of losses since entering combat in the Papuan campaign and nothing would have suited Devine more than to turn around the Allies' losing fortunes in New Guinea. While his B-26s had done considerable damage in New Britain, Devine had been less successful around Buna, like the near disastrous mission on 12 September, to slow the flow of supplies and reinforcements to the Japanese at Ioribaiwa.

Now on this 22 September morning, with this foul weather, Devine could only wait. Maybe the Marauders would still go out; maybe they'd go back to Australia.

Perhaps the busiest site in all of Port Moresby on this damp, gray morning of 22 September was 12 Mile Drome, home of the two American fighter groups in the Papuan campaign, the 8th and 35th. Anybody who had ever come to Port Moresby could not miss 12 Mile Drome, for the airfield always swarmed with aircraft that almost constantly whined in and out of revetment areas, and almost continually took off or landed. If the Airacobras were not taking off to escort bombers, they were taking off to make fighter-bomber attacks against Japanese positions in the Owen Stanleys, or making support strikes for the Australian ground troops in these same jungle mountains. Or, the P-39s were taking off to conduct armed reconnaissance missions or to intercept bombers that came to attack Moresby. Since the Airacobras seemed to be constantly moving, armament trailers, ground crew personnel carriers, jeeps loaded with pilots, or growling fuel trucks never ceased coming in and out of dispersal areas.

Control personnel at the 7 Mile Drome control tower rarely left their high perch, since activities at 7 Mile rarely diminished. This endless, continuous activity at the fighter base had become so common that no one in Moresby any longer paid attention to the hustle and bustle.

On this gray morning, a horde of 35th and 8th Fighter Groups airmen, and even some of the service troops around Moresby, had wandered to revetment areas of the 35th Group's 40th and 39th Squadrons to stare curiously at the oddly designed planes—twin fuselages tapering back to a twin tail, with an engine at the head of each fuselage. For most of these men, this had been the first time they had ever seen close up the P-38 Lightning fighter plane.

"Goddamn," one of the airmen said, "That's the nuttiest thing I ever saw. Does that contraption really fly?"

"They fly all right," a crew chief sergeant answered. "They say it's the fastest thing in the air. They claim it can outdive, outrun, and outclimb a Zero anytime."

"Shit," the visitor scoffed, "nothing can outfly those goddamn Zeros. We ain't never had nothin' to match those Mitsubishi fighter planes."

"Well, they say these babies can do it," the crew

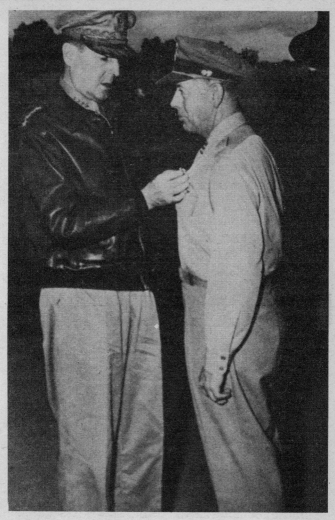

Gen. Douglas MacArthur (L) congratulates Gen. George Kenney (R) for job well done during Operation Providence.

Gen. Basil Morris, commander of the ground troops in New Guinea, could not stem the Japanese tide.

A/C Frank Lukis and his Australian RAAF units could not cope with superior Japanese air force during early air war in New Guinea.

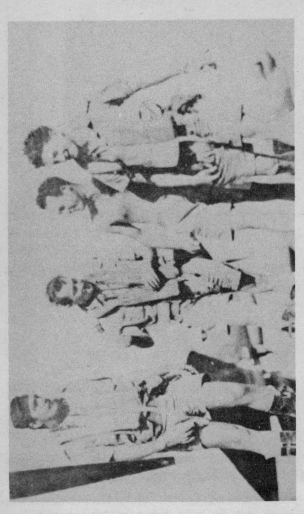

Lt. Larry Jackson, second from left, and other pilots of his RAAF 75 Squadron.

Gen. Ennis Whitehead, ADVON 5th Air Force commander in New Guinea, went for broke during September crises in New Guinea war.

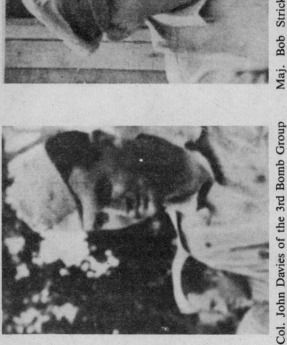

Col. John Davies of the 3rd Bomb Group agreed to try new innovations.

Maj. Bob Strickland of the 3rd Bomb Group led the first parafrag attack against Japanese positions in New Guinea.

General Kenney awards Sgt. Elbert Jones, gunner of Davies' B-25, the Silver Star for his efforts during New Guinea air war.

General Kenney talks to Maj. John Hennebry of 3rd Bomb Group (C) and Capt. Larry Tanberg (R) after the multiple air strikes on 22 Sept. 1942.

Col. Boyd "Buzz" Wagner of the U.S. 8th Fighter Group did a creditable job against superior numbers of Japanese air units.

Lt. Col. Paul "Pappy" Gunn (R) discusses B-25 innovations with Maj. F.H. Smith (L).

Col. Dwight Devine led the 22nd Bomb Group in the B-26s during the New Guinea air campaign.

Capt. Tom Lynch scored heavily against Japanese fighter pilots.

Maj. George Welch had been fighting since Pearl Harbor and the American fighter pilot raised his kill score during Papuan campaign.

Pappy Gunn in his B-25 Commerce Destroyer. Gunn pulled bombardier's compartment and installed ten .50 caliber guns in nose and forward fuselage. The Commerce Destroyer became one of the most devastating U.S. weapons of the Pacific war.

Gen. Hitoshi Imamura, commander of the Japanese forces in the Southwest Pacific, was certain he could capture Port Moresby by driving over the Owen Stanley Mountains.

Adm. Junichi Kasaka, commander of the 24th Air Flotilla, had everything his way during early stages of the Papuan campaign.

Capt. Masahisa Saito, commander of the Tinian Fighter Wing in Lae, had given Allied airmen and ground troops a rough time.

Gen. Tomitaro Horii, commander of the Nankai Shitai Force had driven to within 30 miles of Port Moresby and it appeared that New Guinea was lost.

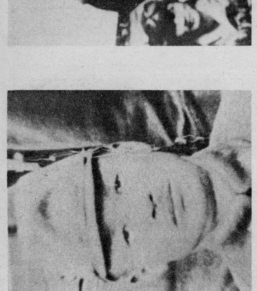

Pilots of the Tinian Wing. These airmen enjoyed a field day in their Zeros against inferior P-40 and P-39 fighter plands of the Allied air forces.

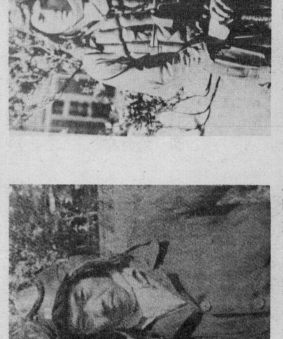

P/O Saburo Saki, a fighter ace of the Tinian Wing.

Lt. Hiroshi Nishizawa, "The Devil," was Japan's greatest air ace. He massacred Allied air units during the Papuan campaign.

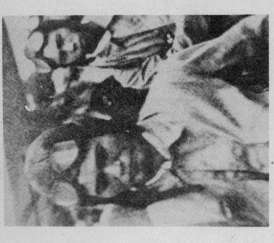

Capt. Uegara Shingo (R) commanded the 24th Air Flotilla's bombers during the Papuan campaign.

Capt. Bunja Shimada led the 4th Kokutai Wing's bombers that continually bombed Port Moresby, the last Allied base in New Guinea

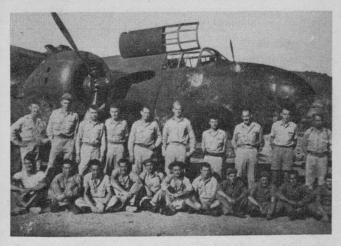

Pilots and gunners of the 3rd Bomb Group's 89th Squadron who carried out first parafrag bomb attacks against the Japanese.

Australian airmen of the RAAF 9th Operational Group had to hold alone against overwhelming numbers during early stages of the New Guinea air war.

Capt. Don Hall, of the 3rd Group's 13th Squadron, briefs airmen before low level bombing attack with medium bombers, a first in the Pacific War.

Port Moresby, New Guinea: this was the prize the Japanese wanted. They would then control everything north of Australia in the Southwest Pacific.

A B-17 of the 43rd Heavy Bomb Group crash lands on the coast after getting shot up by pilots of the Japanese Tinian Wing.

P-40s of the 8th Fighter Group take off from their base in Port Moresby.

3rd Bomb Group armorers install .50 caliber guns on forward fuselage of a B-25. The innovation of putting ten forward firing machine guns on the medium Mitchell bomber became a vital weapon in the Southwest Pacific war.

A parafrag bomb attack on Buna destroyed an array of Japanese planes on the ground.

Heavy Japanese ack ack fire always greeted American airmen when they attacked the Tinian Wing base at Lae.

B-25s of the 3rd Bomb Group devastate Japanese positions in the Owen Stanley Mountains with innovations parafrag bombs.

End of the Buna battle: Japanese prisoners, survivors of the Nankai Shitai Force, sit before their Australian captors.

The U.S. P-38 fighter plane. This aircraft proved superior to the Zero and helped to end Japanese domination of the skies over the Southwest Pacific.

The Japanese base at Buna lies in ruins after the 22 Sept. 1942 Commerce Destroyer air attacks by 3rd Bomb Group.

Natives prepare rough landing field to allow first C-47 to land at Buna with engineers and construction equipment.

GIs of the U.S. 32nd Division cross the Waropi River in pursuit of fleeing Nankai Shitai Japanese troops during the battle for Buna.

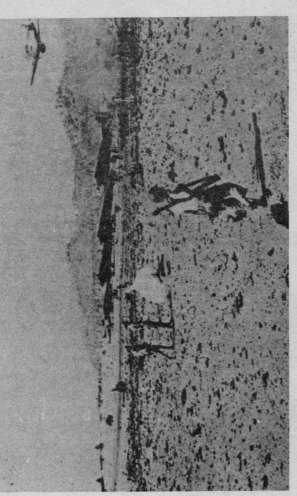

C-47 transport planes bring in supplies to Port Moresby.

American GIs ford a small jungle stream in continued chase of Japanese during the Buna fight.

Battle for Buna did not come easy: American cemetery in Buna, where slain 32nd Division GIs were buried.

chief sergeant said, slapping the wing of one of the P-38s.

In another revetment area, Capt. Tom Lynch stood next to a Lightning with Col. Boyd Wagner of the 8th Fighter Group. "You wouldn't believe it, Colonel," Lynch shook his head. "Not in a hundred years would you believe it."

"It's that good, huh?" Wagner asked.

"It's that good," Captain Lynch nodded. "When we flew these things down in Townsville, they actually scared us. I never knew a plane that climbed that quick, dove so hard, or flew so fast—nearly four hundred miles an hour."

"Four hundred!" Wagner hissed. "Jesus, that's fast."

"Of course, the plane is not as maneuverable as a Zero," Captain Lynch gestured. "But they had some people down in Townsville who had experience with the P-38 in the CBI on an experimental basis. They told us not to dogfight with the Zero; just chase them, or climb up and come diving down at them. They said the best thing was simply to hang high in the sky and shoot down on the Zero."

"You mean this plane can go high enough to outdive a Zero?" Wagner asked.

"We had the P-38 up to forty thousand feet," Lynch answered, "and they responded up there just as good as they did at ten thousand."

Wagner shook his head. "That's something."

"I hear that all our fighter groups will soon change over to P-38s: the rest of the 35th and your own 8th Fighter Group."

169

"Christ," Wagner huffed, "that must be why they had us convert one of our P-39 squadrons to a fighter-bomber squadron with those new parafrag bomb racks under the wings. Major Welch and his boys have been practicing with the new parafrag for quite a while."

"Could be," Lynch nodded. Then he squinted up at the low clouds. "I wish to hell this weather would break, we could try these P-38s in combat."

"It'll clear sooner or later," Buzz Wagner said, "it always does."

"We just got those planes up here yesterday," Captain Lynch said. "Most of the guys can't wait to find out what they'll do."

At 0610 hours, Bent Nose Ennis Whitehead had finished his breakfast at the 5th Air Force ADVON headquarters in the rickety Port Moresby Hotel. With a cup of coffee in his hand, he stood on the warped porch and stared out at the sprawling airbase. The gray morning was cool and Whitehead welcomed the change from the heat and humidity that usually prevailed at Port Moresby. He had just taken another sip of his coffee, when an aide came out on the porch and handed him a radio report.

"General, sir, the first morning recon reports from PBYs."

Whitehead nodded and studied the report. "Christ, it looks like the Japanese are up to something big."

"Yes sir, " the aide said. "The recon reports confirmed the reports of the native scouts that came into ANGAU. The Japanese have brought in a swarm of Bettys to Buna to join their Vals there, maybe a couple squadrons of heavy bombers. They've also brought more Bettys to Gasmata, apparently from Arawe, and they've now got a squadron of Zeros at Gasmata."

Whitehead shook his head. "Those Zeros were brought in to escort those Bettys somewhere, probably Moresby. The bastards. Looks like they want to make the biggest raid yet on Moresby. I knew they were pissed off from that parafrag attack on Ioribaiwa, but I didn't think the tactic would rile them up that much. If they keep us grounded for a few days, those snakes in Ioribaiwa can crawl right down Imita Ridge and into Moresby."

"That seems to be their plan, sir," the aide agreed. He looked up at the gray sky. "Well, they won't be able to come in this morning, and maybe not for a couple of days according to weather reports."

Bent Nose Whitehead stroked his chin. "Captain, go inside to G-2 and find out our complement of aircraft in Port Moresby."

"Yes sir."

The aide had barely left when John Davies pulled up to the porch and alighted from his jeep. As he walked up the steps to meet Whitehead, the general frowned. "What the hell are you doing up so early? And how come you came here?"

"We're finished, Ennis," Davies said, "the B-25s I mean. Pappy's got sixteen of them converted to go along with the other four, twenty converted B-25s. We want to go out right away."

Whitehead squinted at the low clouds. "In this weather?"

"Do you know a better time to catch them off guard? Most of the light bombers in Moresby now have honeycombs to use the parafrag, and I understand that one of the 8th Group's squadrons has also converted. Hell, we can fly under this weather. You've got the cartographer charts. We know the altitude of every peak in the Owen Stanleys and we can come in from the sea or the coastal lowlands to hit Buna, Salamaua, and Lae."

Whitehead referred to the recon report in his hand. "Their bases are jammed with aircraft right now." He took another sip of coffee, looked at the sheet again, and then turned to Davies. "I'd sure like to hit them right now, but I don't know about this weather."

"They're waiting to hit us as soon as the weather clears," Davies said. "We ought to hit them first. The whole idea with the parafrags is to hit at low altitude. We only need a ceiling of a few hundred feet. Pappy Gunn agrees. He's checked over the altimeters on the A-20s and the B-25s to make sure they're okay."

"Pappy's crazy," Whitehead grinned.

Then as Whitehead gulped the last of his coffee, the aide returned and handed the ADVON commander a sheaf of papers, the aircraft complement at Moresby. Heavies: 12 B-17s of the 43rd and 24 B-26s of the 22nd at 7 Mile Drome; light and mediums: 26 A-20s and 30 B-25s of the

172

3rd Bomb Group at 3 Mile Drome, and 26 Beauforts of 22nd Squadron at 4 Mile Drome. Fighters: 50 new P-38s and 25 P-39s of the 35th and 46 P-39s of the 8th Fighter Groups at 12 Mile Drome, along with 30 P-40s of the Australian 75 Squadron at 4 Mile Drome.

"Does the complement of the 8th Fighter Group include those Airacobras converted to parafrag fighter-bombers?" Whitehead asked the aide.

"Yes sir, sixteen of them from their 35th Squadron."

"Christ, we've got over two hundred fifty combat aircraft around here," Whitehead said.

"We've had considerable replacements in the past couple of days."

"Son of a bitch," Whitehead cursed, "if those Bettys and Vals at Buna and Gasmata hit us again, they'll kick the hell out of us."

"As I said, Ennis," Davies said. "We've got twenty B-25s converted and ready."

"How about the other outfits?" Whitehead asked his aide.

"Half of 22 Squadron's have racks and sixteen P-39s from the 8th Group have the same honeycomb racks," the aide said.

"That'll give us plenty of low level punch," Davies persisted.

Whitehead stroked his chin, meditating. Then he looked again at the clouds before turning once more to Davies. "Okay, Johnny, you talked me into it. In fact, we'll go for broke. We'll send out heavies, too. They can hit the runways while you people with the parafrags can hit their parked aircraft."

Davies grinned, but the aide gasped. "But the weather, sir."

"Screw the weather, Whitehead gestured. "We've got four or five squadrons that can make parafrag attacks, and we may as well get the bastards right now. Captain, send a runner to every unit in Moresby. I want all squadron and group commanders here at headquarters for a briefing at 0900. We're going to send out every goddamn plane." He paused. "Then call our staff to the operations room right now, so we can plan multiple strikes for this afternoon."

"But the weather, sir," the aide complained again.

"I suggest you follow the general's request," Davies scolded the aide. "Get the air commanders here on the double."

"Yes sir," the captain answered Colonel Davies.

CHAPTER TEN

At 0700, 22 September, Capt. Uehara Shingo had just finished breakfast at Buna with Cmdr. Bunji Shimada and several other air officers of the 4th Kokutai bomber wing. Shingo felt satisfied with the fare of rice, slabs of fish, tea, and juice. The cooks at Buna had obviously made a special effort because their wing commander had come down from Gasmata to join B Group officers at their meals. Now Shingo and Shimada climbed in a command car, an old American De-Soto sedan that had been imported to Japan before the war. The driver took the 4th Wing officers out to the dispersal and runway areas. When the officers alighted from the sedan, they walked leisurely about the hordes of parked aircraft along the Buna runways, and they occasionally squinted at the many more aircraft, mostly

Vals, that were hidden under the trees some distance from the runways. A few Japanese ground crews working in the area bowed or stiffened with respect as the officers passed. They reverted to their work, however, when Captain Shingo acknowledged them with a gesture.

"Never have we had so many aircraft here in Buna," Captain Shingo said.

"Well over a hundred, Captain," Shimada answered. "We expected a squadron of Mitsubishi fighter planes from the Tinian Wing to join us this morning. Unfortunately, the inclement weather has delayed their flight from Salamaua."

"Fortunately, we brought the G-M 4 bombers here when we did," Captain Shingo said, "and they are now in close proximity to Port Moresby. As soon as we receive favorable weather reports, we will fly at once. Lieutenant Commander Nakajima's 10 Squadron of fighter planes and the heavy bombers from Arawe have also arrived in Gasmata before this foul weather covered the Bismarck Archipelago. I had hoped to carry out these massive strikes yesterday or at least by this morning, but obviously we cannot."

"We have made some minor strikes on Port Moresby during the past two days with our Aichi dive bombers," Commander Shimada said, "but we have caused only minimal damage because of the weather."

"We must simply bide our time," the 4th Kokutai Wing commander said. "The Mitsubishi squadrons at Salamaua, I understand, are prepared to escort your Aichi aircraft as soon as you call on them for your next bombing mission. On your next sortie, I would like you to concentrate your attacks on the enemy's light bombers since the small bomb loads of your dive bombers cannot do enough damage to runways. If fortunes favor us, we will strike with nearly a hundred Mitsubishi heavy bombers on the runways that should certainly destroy the Port Moresby air strips once and for all."

Shimada nodded.

"When we conduct this mission," Shingo said, "the heavy bombers will leave Buna a half hour after your Aichi dive bombers. You should have caused considerable consternation and confusion by the time we arrive for strikes on the runways. The heavy bombers at Gasmata will leave there at the same moment we leave Buna. Thus, they should reach Port Moresby an hour after our A Group heavy bombers to further damage the Port Moresby runways. Fighters from Lae will escort our A Group bombers as fighters from Salamaua will escort your Aichi bombers. Lieutenant Commander Nakajima's 10 Squadron will escort the G-M 4 bombers from Gasmata."

"I see," Shimada said. "And will Captain Saito himself lead the Mitsubishi fighter planes out of Lae to escort your own A Group heavy bombers?"

"Yes," Shingo answered. He pursed his lips. "These strikes will entail the use of all available aircraft in the 4th Kokutai and Tinian Wings. There is an element of chance in leaving our bases undefended. Still, if these massive strikes succeed, we will keep the Moresby airbases out of action for some days. The Nankai Shitai forces can then move into Port Moresby without the hazards of enemy air attacks."

"General Horii is anxious to resume his offensive," Shimada said. "He believes he is now well prepared since new supplies have reached him from Kokoda and Buna, and his troops have enjoyed considerable rest."

"Unfortunately, we cannot control the weather," Shingo said. "We can only wait for the first opportunity."

Then a messenger on a bicycle brought a message to Captain Shingo. He bowed reverently. "Honorable Captain, we have two reports. I knew you would want to read them immediately."

Capt. Uehara Shingo nodded and took the two sheets of paper. He read both of them quickly and then turned to Commander Shimada. "The reports confirm the readiness of our aircraft in Lae, Gasmata, and Salamaua. Captain Saito assures us that two squadrons of his Mitsubishi fighter planes are prepared to leave at once for escort duty of our A Group G-M 4 bombers. All fifty-six aircraft are fully loaded with machine gun belts and 20mm cannon shells. Captain Saito also tells us that the fighter squadrons at Salamaua are equally prepared to escort your Aichi dive bombers as soon as you are ready to leave. You are merely to call Lieutenant Takase at Salamaua to arrange the time and place of rendezvous."

"Excellent," Shimada nodded. "And the

other report?"

"The second report is from Gasmata. It is the confirmation that our two squadrons of G-M 4 bombers that came from Arawe are fully loaded with five hundred pound bombs and they await orders to take off. The report from Gasmata also indicates that Lieutenant Commander Nakajima has his fighter planes fully loaded with machine gun belts and 20mm shells. He and his pilots, too, are ready to man their aircraft at once."

"Then we need only await favorable weather," Commander Shimada said.

Shingo nodded. "Meanwhile, we would do well to urge our pilots and crews to relax. Our meteorologists at Rabaul are continually monitoring this weather pattern and they will notify us at once when the weather begins to clear. Such improvements in the weather may come as soon as this afternoon, or perhaps tomorrow. We have an advantage."

"An advantage?" Shimada asked.

"Since the weather fronts move south," Shingo said, "our meteorologists in Rabaul can inform us of a clearing trend much sooner than can the enemy's weather men in Port Moresby predict a clearing trend to aid their own air commanders."

Shimada grinned. "This is indeed an advantage, Captain. This will mean that our aircraft can be airborne and perhaps even making their attacks before the enemy air commanders even get a report on possible weather changes."

Shingo once more surveyed the swarms of planes about him and then turned to the B Group commander. "Come, Bunji, we will return to your quarters for a refreshing cup of tea."

"An excellent idea, Captain," the moon-faced Shimada answered.

Captain Uehara had not considered the brazen, gambling Gen. Ennis Whitehead or the brash, persevering John Davies when the 4th Kokutai Wing Commander rode leisurely back to Commander Shimada's quarters for a cup of tea. By 0900 hours, while Shingo and Shimada perhaps enjoyed a second cup of tea at Buna, some two dozen group and squadron leaders of the 5th Air Force had arrived at the ADVON mess hall in the Port Moresby Hotel dining room. The visitors sat on benches in pairs or small groups, wondering why their commander had called this sudden briefing. The babbling continued even when Whitehead himself entered the room with aides who carried rolled up charts and a framework of 2x4s. The chatter merely diminished in decibels, but did not stop.

Whitehead made no effort to quiet his combat commanders until an aide fastened the framework behind the general and a second aide unwound a huge map and pinned the map to the framework. When the aides finished, Whitehead turned a bright light on the map and then looked at his air officers.

"Okay, we're ready," Whitehead bellowed. His deep gravel voice, rising above the chatter, abruptly stopped the talk among the men of 5th

Air Force.

"All of you should be familiar with this chart behind me," Whitehead gestured. "Not only does the chart pinpoint the Japanese air bases in New Guinea and Gasmata, but the chart also marks the altitude of the various peaks in the Owen Stanleys. Take a good look. My aides will pass out small copies of this chart and you'd better study them thoroughly. And hang on to them," he gestured, "because you're going to need them."

The men only listened.

Whitehead now picked up the pointer and tapped a point on the map. "Here's the Buna coastal area. You can see the lowland plains come inland for twenty to forty mile widths at Buna and Salamaua." He moved the pointer to another part of the map. "The low plain extends thirty miles from the coast at Lae, all the way up the Markham Valley. And of course, up here," he moved the pointer up the map, "you can come all the way across the Solomon Sea to Gasmata."

"What are you driving at, sir," Capt. Tom Lynch suddenly spoke.

"I'm talking about making an air strike on these bases as soon as possible," Whitehead said. "Today; right after noon mess."

"W-what?" somebody hissed. "In this weather? My God! we couldn't even get over the Owen Stanleys."

"That's why I'm handing out the contour maps and telling you to study them. Of course," he grinned slyly, "I wouldn't ask anybody to go who hasn't got an altimeter in his aircraft."

No one answered the general.

"The map we'll hand out is quite accurate," Whitehead continued. "I guarantee it. The cartographers have been over those Owen Stanleys several times, checking and rechecking to verify their figures."

Still, no one said anything to the 5th ADVON general.

"Now," Whitehead gestured, "we'll conduct the same kind of multiple strikes on those airbases as the Japanese pulled on us last month. If we succeed, we can maintain the pressure. They don't have the heavy equipment that we have to get their airstrips back in shape in a hurry. They're still using Rabaul laborers or Papuans when they can find any to repair runways with shovels and pails for the most part. They need at least a week to patch up an airstrip. We'll hound them as often as we can, whenever we can get off for new strikes, to make sure they can't get their runways back in commission. They'll be caught in a vicious circle: no interceptors to stop us because they have no runways, and no runways to launch any planes. Anyway, if this mission comes off right, they won't have many planes left to launch. Right now, their airbases are jammed with planes because they're apparently getting ready for another strike on Moresby. We'll have to beat them to the punch."

The men still listened in silence.

"If the mission succeeds," Whitehead continued, "we'll be able to concentrate on hitting their ground troops and supply lines in the Owen Stanleys while we support the Australian ground troops." He paused and then gestured. "We've taken count and we have all the aircraft we need for these strikes. Twelve B-17s of the 19th Bomb Group are flying up from Cape Horn and they should be at 7 Mile Drome any time now. They'll be loaded and gassed up to fly out at noon, just like the rest of us."

"Are we going to use every plane in Moresby?" A/C Frank Lukis asked.

"Everything we can mount in the air," Whitehead answered. "We're going to conduct a two phase attack on the New Guinea targets: heavies to knock out the runways and the lighter bombers to destroy as many of their planes as possible. We'll do the same thing at Gasmata."

"Gasmata?" somebody cried.

"Yes," Whitehead answered, "Gasmata. We want to knock out the runway there as well as the ones in Papua. Our reports indicate they've moved new Bettys and Zeros to Gasmata. Our information is that both Gasmata and Buna are packed with bombers, a lot of them under the trees. So both enemy air bases are nice fat targets. Our aircraft with the parafrags can come in low enough to even find the planes they keep under the trees and knock them out as well as planes out in the open along the runways. I'm having incendiary frags sent to the 3rd Group, 22 Squadron, and 8th Group dromes. I'll want these air units to use incendiary as well as fragmentation bombs on their parachutes."

Neither Colonel Davies, Commander Lukis,

nor Major Welch answered Whitehead. They merely listened with deepening curiosity.

"Okay," Whitehead said before he turned to an aide. "Captain, I want you to pass around the maps as well as the field order on this mission for early this afternoon."

The captain nodded and passed out the sheets with a sergeant aide of his own. Whitehead then spoke again to his commanders.

"These strikes must be timed precisely. We've got to hit all the Jap bases at once, along with another strike on Ioribaiwa. That means we'll need to alter take off time to hit at exactly 1400 hours. Those of you going to Buna leave here at about 1300 hours. Those going to Lae and Salamaua can leave at about 1230 hours. The aircraft going to Gasmata will need to be off by noon, and those going to Ioribaiwa will only need fifteen minutes, so you can eat a late lunch. We've already notified your units to have your airmen in their briefing tents by 100 hours. You can go directly from here to meet with them. Meanwhile, we've notified your engineering and ordnance personnel to start readying your aircraft. You're likely to find them fully bombed up, fueled, and loaded with strafing belts by the time you return to your units."

"You're working awfully fast, sir," a squadron leader said. "You're not giving us time to catch our breath."

"If I give you time to catch your breath, Captain," the general said, "we may not catch the bastards asleep. Yes," Whitehead nodded, "this is short notice. But our staff at ADVON has been working since 0630 to prepare the field order. We've planned this mission pretty well."

The men now studied the FO sheets and Whitehead paused a moment before he continued. "Okay, we'll start with Gasmata." He looked at Col. Dwight Devine. "You can see your mission, Dwight. You've got to saturate the Gasmata runways, even though you may have to do so at low level. I want your Marauders carrying thousand pounders so you can dig volcano craters in the goddamn Nip airstrips."

Colonel Devine nodded.

"You have hit from low level, Dwight."

"Yes," Devine nodded. "We don't like it, but we can do so if we have to. We'll fly our three plane Vs fifteen seconds behind each other. With three planes in each drop, it won't take long to finish those runways."

"Good," Whitehead said. "We'd like to hit some of those swarms of parked aircraft reported there, but your first priority is the runways, so their planes can't take off. Anyway maybe Captain Lynch can make some low level runs on parked aircraft."

Now the men looked at the 35th Group squadron leader, who merely shuttled his glance between Whitehead and the FO sheet in his hand.

"That's right, Captain, it's in your FO," Whitehead said. "I want you to escort the 22nd to Gasmata with those new P-38s. Those Lightnings have wonderful range from what I hear, and I'm told they can deal effectively with Zeros. Maybe you'll get a chance to prove it. If you don't run into interceptors, you can do some damage with your strafing guns and those 37mm cannon on the P-38s."

"We'll do our best, sir," Capt. Tom Lynch promised.

Tom Lynch had come overseas with the original cadre of the 35th Fighter Group in March of 1942, when the group left the west coast of the U.S. He had been in training for more than a year with the group. He went into his first combat as a young lieutenant in the 35th's 39th Squadron, where he was now the CO. On his first combat, he had shot down one Zero and chased off another one in damaged condition, a remarkable feat for a green pilot flying against seasoned enemy pilots in superior fighter planes. Lynch continued to show courage and leadership qualities since his first combat and by early July he had downed his 11th plane and he had been appointed squadron leader of the 39th Squadron. He was expecting promotion to major at any day.

"You can see from your FO sheet, the time and location of your rendezvous with the 22nd," Whitehead told the 39th Squadron leader. "I'd like at least thirty of those P-38s on escort. Can you manage that?"

"Yes sir," Lynch answered. "We'll use both the 39th and 40th Squadrons."

General Whitehead nodded and then looked at John Davies. "Well, Johnny, today you try out those B-25s. You can fill the bomb bays with parafrags and fill those ten guns with strafing belts to hit Buna. Jesus, with that kind of fire power, you ought to knock out every plane in Buna, and there's sure a lot of them there."

Big John Davies only grinned.

"You'll be going along with the 43rd Group. The heavies will go in first to chop up the Buna runway with thousand pounders. They may have to come low, but they've hit from low level before. As soon as they make their bomb run over the runways, you make your tree top sweep with the B-25 to knock out as many of their parked Bettys and Vals as you can, including any under the trees."

"It'll be a good test, Ennis," Davies said.

"Can you take at least twelve of those converted Mitchells?"

"We'll take sixteen of them, at least," Davies answered.

"Good. The more the better." Then Whitehead looked at Col. Richard Legg, CO of the 35th Fighter Group. "Dick, I want you to take a P-39 squadron to escort the 3rd and 43rd to Buna, while your P-38s are off to Gasmata. I know you've only got a couple dozen P-39s, but our reports indicate there aren't any Zeros in Buna at the moment. In fact, maybe you can even do some strafing yourself if you don't tangle with Nip fighter planes."

"Okay, Ennis," Colonel Legg said.

"You can see your time and place of rendezvous with the bombers going to Buna. Any questions, Dick?"

"No."

"Johnny?" Whitehead turned to Davies again.

"No. This FO is pretty well detailed."

"I'd like the converted A-20s of the 3rd Group along with the 19th Group's B-17s to hit Lae," Whitehead gestured. "This may be a most dangerous mission because the goddamn place has been the biggest Zero nest in the SWPA, and their pilots are good, real good. If you don't surprise them at Lae, we could lose a lot of planes. As you can see, the FO for Lae is pretty clear. Carmichael comes in first to chop up the runways with his B-17s. Then the converted A-20s come in with parafrags to destroy as many of those parked Zeros as they can find. How many Havocs can you send, Johnny?"

Davies turned to Maj. Robert Strickland. "Bob?"

"We can get at least a couple dozen out, sir," Strickland said. "We can do a hell of a lot of damage with twenty-four A-20s loaded with parafrags."

"I'll see for myself," Whitehead said, "because I'll be going along."

Raised eyebrows came from the seated airmen, but no one spoke.

Whitehead turned to Buzz Wagner. "Buzz, I'm giving you the escort assignment for the strike on Lae. You told me you have about forty-five P-39s. That right?"

"About that," Wagner nodded, "but Major Welch's squadron has those parafrag bomb racks. He won't go with us, will he?"

"No," Whitehead said, "he'll be going to

Ioribaiwa."

"Then we'll have at least twenty-four P-39s for escort duty," Wagner said.

"Make that twenty-five," Whitehead pointed. "I'll be flying with you myself." Wagner did not answer and the general continued. "This is a tough assignment, Buzz. If those B-17s or A-20s get jumped by Zeros—God I don't even want to think about it."

"We'll handle it, General," Wagner said.

"Okay," the general nodded. "You can see your rendezvous point is just northwest of Wau at 1330 hours."

"We'll be on time," Wagner said.

Whitehead grinned and turned to A/C Frank Lukis of the RAAF 22 Squadron. "Commander, the Salamaua show goes to you and Captain Tanberg of the 38th Bomb Group. The Salamaua base is just as important as any of these other strikes. They usually keep at least a squadron of fighter planes there and sometimes two. If any of those Zeros get off the ground, they'll raise hell with us."

"Yes sir," Lukis answered. He felt a measure of satisfaction. The Australians had often complained of being relegated to secondary missions, taking a back seat to American air group. But this mission today would be as important as the others.

Capt. Larry Tanberg felt excited. The 38th Bomb Group Sunsetters would finally get into action. He hoped his 71st Squadron of the 38th would do well on this first combat mission. He felt a little uneasy about the nose guns that had been installed in his own B-25s and the parafrag bombs in the bomb bay. But, if the 3rd Bomb Group could succeed with these new Commerce Destroyers, he was certain that he and his 38th Bomb Group would also succeed.

"Commander," Whitehead addressed Lukis again, "When you get back to four mile drome, you'll find sixteen of your Beauforts loaded with frag bombs."

"Yes sir," Lukis answered.

Whitehead then looked at Tanberg. "The 22 Squadron will come in first and you follow. I expect your more heavily armed B-25s to do most of the damage."

"We'll be all right, sir," Tanberg answered.

"Our Beauforts will give them a good show," Lukis said.

"I'm sure you will," Whitehead said. He then turned to Larry Jackson. "Lieutenant, your 75 Squadron will escort the 22 Squadron and B-25s of the 38th Group with your P-40s. I believe you have about thirty of them. These B-25s under Captain Tanberg will be on their first combat mission, so they'll especially need good fighter support."

"Yes sir," Jackson said. "We can get off at least a couple dozen Kittyhawks, and we'll keep a sharp escort around the B-25s."

"I needn't remind you, Lieutenant," the general gestured, "that your mission parallels that of Colonel Wagner. If any of those Zeros get off from Salamaua before Beauforts and B-25s hit, we could be in for some awful losses. It's imperative that you keep enemy fighter planes away from the bombers, if we're to knock out Salamaua."

"We won't fail, sir," Jackson said.

Whitehead nodded. "Please refer to the FO sheet for your time and route of attack." Then Whitehead looked at Maj. George Welch, and with a somewhat admiring gleam. Whitehead knew well the major's background and he held him in the highest esteem.

Welch had begun his career in combat at Pearl Harbor where he had downed two Japanese planes on 7 December 1941. He had then joined the 17th Pursuit Group in the Philippines with Buzz Wagner. Welch had also moved out of the Philippines with the evacuated 17th Pursuit unit, and he had then fought in Java against heavy odds. Day after day, Welch and other pilots had flown out of Surabaja, Java, but their efforts had been as futile in Java as such efforts had been in the Philippines. In late February, Welch and 12 other P-40 pilots ran into 50 Japanese Zeros. The Japanese had shot down seven of the P-40s and had so badly damaged the major's own plane, that he had barely sputtered back to Surabaja.

When the opportunity came to join the 8th Group in Townsville, Major Welch had accepted the assignment. He was delighted to find Col. Boyd Buzz Wagner in charge of the new U.S. Air Force fighter group.

Welch had listened to the reports of the A-20 frag bomb attacks on Ioribaiwa with a tinge of envy, for he had been practicing himself with the parafrag bomb and he had hoped to be among the first to use the new tactic. Now he would find himself in the enviable position of raising hell against the Japanese who had caused him so much distress for the first six months of the war.

"Major," Whitehead said, "I hope you and your pilots have familiarized yourselves with the use of the parafrag."

"We sure have, sir," Welch said.

"You can see that you have the shortest run — Ioribaiwa. But it's important. We want that forward Japanese ground position hit hard again and again and again — until there's only ashes at Ioribaiwa. They're too close to Moresby for comfort. Maybe you can make two or three strikes on the positions this afternoon."

"We'll go out as many times as we can, sir; as fast as they reload us with strafing belts and parafrags."

"You can see your mission on the FO," Whitehead said. "Naturally, you won't need escort. If you run into any Zeros, salvo your bombs and take care of yourselves."

"We'll be okay, sir," Major Welch said.

Now Whitehead scanned the entire body of group and squadron leaders. "Be sure everybody in your units studies the maps carefully. We don't want anybody hitting an Owen Stanley peak on the way to target. You can fly over the clouds for most of the way, but you'll need to come in low at least twenty-five or thirty miles from target to avoid detection." He paused. "Any questions?"

None.

"Okay, then let's recap. The 22nd hits Gasmata and they'll be escorted by the P-38s of the 35th Group's 39th and 40th Squadrons. The bombers should leave at noon to reach target at 1400. The Forts of the 19th and the A-20s of the 3rd Group will strike Lae. Colonel Wagner's 80th Squadron will provide escort. Commander Lukis will use his 22 Squadron Beauforts to strike Salamaua, with 75 Squadron P-40s as escorts. These bomber units should leave at 1230 hours. The 43rd's B-17s and the 3rd's B-25s will strike Buna, under escort of Colonel Legg's 41st Squadron. These bombers should be off at 1300 hours to reach Buna at the 1400 hour time. The 8th Group's 35th Squadron will strike Ioribaiwa as often as they can with parafrag bombs." He paused. "Now, again, any questions?"

Before anyone answered, the airmen in the hotel mess hall heard the drone of planes overhead. Everyone here guessed that the drones had come from the 19th Group's B-17s just arriving from Cape Horn, Australia, after their flight over the Coral Sea. The drone of Fortresses reminded all of them that this planned multiple mission, in this inclement weather, was only some three hours away. When the roar of B-17s faded somewhere to the eastward toward 7 Mile Drome, Whitehead closed the briefing.

"If there are no more questions," he now spoke softly, "I'd suggest you get back to your units to brief your crews and pilots. Then you'd best have a quick lunch. All I can add—good luck to all of you."

The squadron and group leaders rose from their benches in silence and just as silently they left the 5th ADVON mess hall. Whitehead and his aides stood and watched them depart. When the air commanders were gone, Bent Nose turned to one of his staff aides.

"Bring my jeep around. I've got a briefing at 12 Mile Drome with the 8th Fighter Group."

"Yes sir," the aide answered.

CHAPTER ELEVEN

At precisely noontime, the big Marauder engines of the 22nd Bomb Group ignited in multiple explosions across 7 Mile Drome like the roars of angry bulls. Colonel Devine and his B-26 crews would take off first from Moresby on this gloomy 22 December day. Ground crews had fully loaded bomb bays with two thousand pound bombs and loaded guns in the nose, tail, and turret gun positions with full complements of .50 caliber strafing belts. The 24 Marauders would make the longest journey today, all the way over the Owen Stanleys and then across the wide expanse of the Solomon Sea to Gasmata. Pilots and crews felt apprehensive. Somehow, they could not quite believe that they would cross the width of eastern Papua and the Japanese patrolled Solomon Sea without enemy detection.

Not Colonel Devine, not his pilots, and not his combat crews really believed the Japanese would simply sleep this afternoon and allow the B-26s to drone unopposed over Gasmata to destroy their runways. Yes, the high number of parked aircraft at Gasmata made a fat target. At least a squadron of Zeros had been reported there. Would they get airborne to knock the B-26s out of the sky? The Marauders would need to come at low level, possibly under a thousand feet. They themselves could be fat targets for anti-aircraft fire as well as diving enemy fighter planes. The 22nd Group crews remembered too vividly their recent near extinction when they attacked the Buna resupply convoy on 12 September.

As the B-26s lumbered down the taxiways, rocking like giant armadillos, the men on the ground felt as tense as the Marauder crews. They could see the sober faces of the turret gunner, the pilot and co-pilot in the cabin, and the tail gunners. No one in the 22nd relished this combat flight on a day that normally kept aircraft grounded; a day, in fact, when 5th ADVON had cancelled all air missions early this morning.

Colonel Devine and the pilot of a companion B-26, now at the head of the runway, revved the twin engines of their Marauders until the air controller in the tower blinked his green light. The two B-26s roared down the airstrip, vibrating the ground under them, before they rose like huge balloons and turned slightly left and up toward Imita Ridge beyond the lowlands of Moresby. Soon, in pairs, other B-26s also roared down the runway and hoisted themselves into the air before banking right and upward toward Imita Ridge. The ground crews at 7 Mile Drome caught them airborne for only a moment for they quickly disappeared into the clouds. The B-26s would climb until they cleared the overcast and they would then drone northward.

By 1210 hours, all 24 Marauders were gone.

At 1240 hours came the strangest sight ever seen in Moresby. Not only ground crewmen of the 8th Fighter Group at 12 Mile Drome, but service troops from other units had stopped their vehicles to ogle at the strange contraptions rocking along the taxiways — P-38 Lightnings of the group's 39th and 40th Squadrons, 30 of them. Men on the ground gaped. Even the pilots of the 8th's 41st Squadron, who would be taking off in P-39s, watched with a mixture of curiosity and uncertainty. Among them were Col. Buzz Wagner and Gen. Ennis Whitehead. They watched with the same awe as the lowest airmen as the Lightnings moved like huge spiders toward the head of the runway.

"They're something, aren't they General?" Wagner said.

"Goddamn," Whitehead shook his head. "Those are the craziest things I ever saw. But I'm told they can put the Zero to shame. We'll know for sure before the day is over."

The first two P-38s whirled onto the head of the runway, Capt. Tom Lynch's lead Lightning and that of his wingman, Lt. Robert Faurot. As the pilots waited for the take off signal, they revved their engines and the screams burst across 12 Mile Drome with such high pitched intensity that spectators felt a numbness in their ears.

Strange craft indeed: twin fuselages, twin tails, twin engines, with the cockpit in the center of the tic-tac-toe design.

If any spectator at 12 Mile doubted the rumors of the P-38s ability, such doubts were soon dispelled. When the green light blinked from the control tower, Captain Lynch and Lieutenant Faurot released the brakes of their Lightnings. The P-38s zoomed down the field as though shot from a cannon. The speed was astonishing. In a matter of seconds the P-38s were off, arching and shooting upward like rockets. Those on the field saw them for only a few seconds before the P-38s disappeared into the clouds. Weird or not, the speed and climb of the P-38 was awesome.

The other P-38s of the 39th and 40th Squadrons also roared down the field with blinding speed and then climbed with astonishing velocity. When the P-38s were gone, Col. Buzz Wagner turned to Whitehead. "Did you ever see anything like that?"

Whitehead shook his head. "One thing is certain. If Devine or his B-26 crews are apprehensive about this strike to Gasmata, I don't think they'll need to worry about their escorts." He suddenly grinned. "You know, I wish I was flying one of those things myself. Christ, I'd love to see the faces of those Jap pilots if they tangle with those Lightnings."

"Come on, sir," Wagner cocked his head, "let's

get a cup of coffee. We'll be taking off ourselves pretty soon — unless you've changed your mind."

"I'm not changing my mind," Whitehead huffed.

At 1230 hours, heavy B-17 engines roared in a deafening din as 12 B-17s of the 19th Bomb Group moved like lumbering giants along the taxiways of 7 Mile Drome. The four engine bombers were more heavily loaded today than usual, with six 1,000 pound bombs in their bays, two more than usual. But then, the Forts would only need to fly to Lae, 250 miles one way. They needed much less fuel, so the B-17s could carry another ton of bombs. 19th Group ground crews, nonetheless, watched uneasily as the big Forts turned in pairs onto the long 7 Mile Drome runway.

"Goddamn," one of the airmen said, "they never carried a load like that before. You think they'll get off all right?"

"They've got reduced gas supply, so they should," a companion said.

The first man squinted up at the low clouds. "But Jesus, they'll have to bomb right on top of that Lae runway with six thousand pounders. Christ, they could be blown right into Huon Gulf."

"Carmichael knows what he's doing. Hell, he's bombed right at sea level."

"One thing is sure," the first man said. "With loads like that they ought to chop that Lae runway to pieces."

"That's the idea," the companion said.

The two ground crewmen, along with dozens of others, watched the B-17s, in pairs, rev their engines before they roared down the long runway. The spectators held their breath, hoping the Forts got off instead of running right off the airstrip and plowing into the kunai fields beyond. But the steady, ever reliable B-17s responded with their extra bomb loads. They rose from the runway and then circled to the north. Soon, the 12 B-17s of the 19th had disappeared into the clouds. The 12 heavies would join the A-20s of the 3rd Group before all 36 bombers droned on to Lae.

At the same 1230 hours on this muggy, cloudy 22 September afternoon, the ignition of A-20 engines exploded across the vast Port Moresby base. Once more engines screamed in revving warm-ups before decelerating to sputtering idleness. The 3rd Group's 89th Squadron Havocs under Maj. Bob Strickland bounced across the rough taxiways at 3 Mile Drome. And again, airmen on the ground stared curiously at the protruding six .50 caliber guns in the noses and wings. They also ogled at the honeycombs under the aircraft, with their white balls of parafrags, as though the bellies of these Havocs had nurtured some kind of strange, giant insect larva under their fuselages.

As the 24 A-20s prepared to take off, ground crews watched with apprehension. Anxiety also prevailed in the hearts of the two man pilot-gunner crews inside of the A-20s. True, they had hit a low level only yesterday with the parafrag bombs without difficulty. But they had enjoyed the element of surprise and Ioribaiwa was not Lae. The 3rd Group crews had seldom attacked Lae without losses and now, the Japanese in Lae might be expecting a parafrag attack similar to the one at Ioribaiwa. Zeros could be waiting like angry hawks over Lae. Further, the Japanese pilots were adept and aggressive. This low level strike could be a suicide mission. Still, if the Americans knocked out Lae, they could hit the Japanese supply lines along the Kokoda Trail with near immunity from fighter interception.

Within 15 minutes, all 24 A-20s were airborne and had disappeared into the clouds.

The 89th Squadron Havocs had been airborne about a half hour, and they had joined the 19th's B-17s, when another burst of aircraft engines exploded at Moresby. 25 P-39s of the 8th Fighter Group's 80th Squadron now taxied slowly toward the main runway at 12 Mile Drome. Hordes of ground crews had lined the runway, sitting in personnel carriers, command cars, jeeps. They watched curiously, for behind Colonel Wagner's lead P-39 came a P-39 piloted by Old Man Whitehead himself. The men had heard that Whitehead had often gone out on combat missions, but as many airmen considered the rumor fiction as those airmen who considered the rumor a fact. Today, however, they saw with their own eyes: the grizzly ADVON commander was indeed in the cockpit of the Airacobra that wheeled onto the runway with Col. Boyd Wagner.

Soon, the control tower at 12 Mile blinked green. Colonel Wagner and General Whitehead zoomed down the runway and veered upward and away. Now, the main show over, those along the runway merely watched nonchalantly as 22 other Airacobras also zoomed down the runway in pairs and arched upward. Finally, the last P-39 of the 8th's 80th Squadron, alone, zoomed down the runway and took off.

"The Old Man may get more than he bargained for," one of the ground crewmen said.

"Hell, he's got guts," a companion answered. "Anyway, it's good to have him up there. The other pilots know that Whitehead will do anything he asks them to do."

"Yeh, I guess," the first man nodded.

At exactly 1330 hours, Col. Boyd Wagner joined the 3rd Group's A-20s and the 19th Group's B-17s at the rendezvous point 25 miles northwest of Wau. Whitehead grinned. His 8th Group colonel was good, real good. He picked up his radio and called him.

"Buzz, I'll take two of the flights and hang with the Havocs; you can take the other and hang with the Forts."

"Okay, Ennis," Wagner answered.

A few minutes later, Maj. Bob Strickland saw the Airacobras coming up on either side of his A-20 formations. When the major squinted from his cabin window and saw the wrinkled face in the P-39 cockpit off to his left, he grinned. Goddamn! The Old Man did come along. Well, Whitehead might get a good lesson in New Guinea combat and maybe he'd appreciate this hard air war. Strickland then leaned back in his cabin and relaxed.

At 1230 hours, while American bombers had taxied toward runways, the twin engines of Beauforts at 4 Mile Drome had also taxied toward a runway. Ground crews did not like the sound of the 22 Squadron engines that strained more than usual, perhaps from the heavy 2,000 pound bomb loads. Still, these Australians knew their Beauforts must take off, must carry these heavy loads, and must destroy the Japanese base at Salamaua.

The Australians had been somewhat bitter since they came under the command of Whitehead, for they believed the ADVON general had relegated them to a secondary role to American air units. Actually, however, until the initiation of the parafrag, Whitehead had not believed that any fighter or light bomb unit could really do much damage to airdromes and only mediums or heavies had been used for these purposes. Obviously, the Australians could not complain today, for they drew an important target in the Zero nest at Salamaua.

The crews of the Beauforts had absorbed Lukis's warning at their briefing: "Remember those poor Diggers at Imita Ridge." The Australians in New Guinea perhaps held a much greater sympathy for the Digger infantrymen than did the Americans, and they knew perhaps more than the Americans the importance of stopping Japanese air attacks and stopping Japanese ground attacks. Finally, the endangered land to the south, Australia, was their homeland, not the homeland of the Americans.

Now the heavily laden Beauforts, 16 of them, turned onto the head of the runway at 4 Mile Drome. The Aussie ground crews held their breath when the first two roared down the strip. But despite heavy engine strains, the aircraft rose skyward with their 2,000 pound loads. The ground crews ogled at the strange honeycombs under their fuselages and filled with packed parafrags, with small white domes protruding like white warts.

Right behind the Beauforts came the 12 B-25s of the 38th Bomb Group. Capt. Larry Tanberg and his co-pilot stared at the huge protruding guns in the nose and wondered if the weapons would disturb the take-off. But Tanberg's Mitchell soared gracefully off the runway and into the sky. Then excitement washed through the tall body of the 71st Squadron leader. At last, the Sunsetters would get a crack at the Japanese.

Finally, a half hour later, at the same Jackson 4 Mile Drome, 26 P-40s of 75 Squadron screamed down the runways under the command of Lt. Larry Jackson. The Kittyhawks carried fully loaded strafing guns and fully loaded 20mm cannons. Again, Aussie ground crews stood about the runway and watched. Not until the last P-40 had disappeared into the clouds did a quiet descend over 4 Mile. Then, one of the ground crewmen turned to a companion.

"It ain't right," he said. "Those Beaus shouldn't be carrying that kind 'a load. And those frags: our lads ain't had that much practice with 'em."

"Beaus have carried two thousand pounds before," the companion said.

"But they could meet a swarm 'a bloody Nips over Salamaua, and them with only twenty-six Kittyhawks to 'elp out. It ain't right," the ground crewman said again. "White'ead is puttin' us in a bind, 'e is; just don't care about us at all. Their Bostons and Mitchells ain't overloaded. 'Ow come they've put those loads on our light Beaus? 'Ow come?"

"Because White'ead ain't got any more heavies to do this job this afternoon," the companion said. "Anyway, this strike on Salamaua will be a good Aussie show, it will. And we'll prove we're just as good as them Yanks."

"I just 'ope we see the lads come back," the first man said.

"They will," the companion said. "Lukis and Jackson are the best."

At 1300 hours on this gloomy day, the 16 B-25s of the 3rd Group's 13th and 8th Squadrons growled out of their revetment areas and rocked slowly along the taxi strips of 3 Mile Drome. Spectators looked in awe at the weirdly adorned aircraft: ten .50 caliber guns jutting from the noses and fuselages, with the bombardier and ball turret compartments strangely missing. The converted B-25s, in fact, only carried three men crews. The pilot would act as his own bombardier, the co-pilot would act as navigator, and the top turret gunner would be their only protection. When the line of 16 Mitchells reached the end of the taxiway, Davies whirled the lead B-25 onto the patched runway, revving his engine while he waited for a green light from the control tower.

Davies' co-pilot, Lt. Ray Wilkins, sat uneasily in his seat, peering apprehensively at the six guns in the hose. He then leaned to the right and stared at the two .50 caliber guns on his side of the fuselage. Wilkins was not sure the Mitchells could get off the ground with the heavy array of loaded guns.

Sgt. Elbert Jones, the turret gunner, felt nervous, too. How could a medium bomber really attack at tree top level? And he wondered how his twin .50s, the only defense on this weird plane, could stave off a swarm of Zeros that might certainly dive down on him. And if the B-25 got hit at this low altitude, the Mitchell would surely crash, killing all aboard. But then, perhaps instant death was better than bailing out over the Owen Stanleys to die a slow death from disease and starvation in the hostile jungle.

When Davies released the brake and the B-25 roared down the airstrip, Jones jerked and then shook, for the plane bounced like an old truck on the washboard runway. Both Sergeant Jones and Lieutenant Wilkins sat rigid, stiffened in anxiety. Even Davies showed a tinge of uneasiness on his face. But as Davies pulled back the wheel, the B-25 responded and hoisted itself skyward to easily clear the trees some 2,000 yards beyond the end of the runway.

By 1320 hours, all 16 Mitchells had jelled into four V formations of three planes each above the clouds at Port Moresby, with Capt. Donald Hall leading the 13th Squadron as Davies himself led 8th Squadron.

When the B-25s had disappeared, a 3rd Group mechanic turned to a companion. "Jesus, those Nips in Buna will sure as hell get a surprise."

"Yeh," his companion said, stroking his chin, "if Zeros don't catch them first."

Again at 7 Mile Drome at the same 1300 hours, 12 B-17s of the 43rd Bomb Group had been warming up its engines for nearly a half hour, screaming like giant auks and nearly deafening the ground crewmen who waited for their Fortresses to take off. Maj. William James Benn, leading these dozen B-17s, did not like the heavy bomb load of six thousand pounders, nor did he like the half empty gas tanks. But he recognized the need to knock out Buna. At almost the same moment that Davies' converted B-25s were taking off at Koki Drome, the green light blinked from the control tower of 7 Mile Drome. The 43rd's major revved his engine and then roared his B-17 down the runway, with a companion B-17 at his side.

By 1310 hours, all twelve of the 43rd's Flying Fortresses were airborne. When they had ducked into the clouds, the ground crews broke up and ambled back to their temporary camp sites in Moresby. Few of them were certain the Forts could hit Buna by surprise and without interception by Japanese Zeros. These ground crewmen did not like the idea of bombing the new, big Buna base at such a low level under the clouds, perhaps below a thousand feet. They just hoped the 12 Forts and their crews came home safely.

Shortly after the 3rd's B-25s and the 43rd's B-17s took off, 24 P-39s of the 35th Fighter Group's 41st Squadron whined like giant, restless chicks. Engines whirled in alternate high and low pitched whines, shuttering wings and vibrating fuselages. The two dozen Airacobras would escort the 3rd Group Mitchells and the 43rd's Fortresses on the Buna Mission.

Col. Richard Legg himself led the 24 P-39s of his 41st Squadron and within 15 minutes the Airacobras had taken off to join the strange looking B-25s and the heavily loaded B-17s already droning above the clouds and over the Owen Stanleys toward Buna.

Legg and his fighter pilots felt an unusual eagerness this afternoon—curious to see how Mitchell bombers, flying as low as fighter-bombers, could make powerful tree top level punches. The idea had mitigated the usual fear of Zeros that often met these pilots over the Owen Stanleys.

When the P-39s loomed from the south and joined the bomber formations, Col. Dick Legg studied the 3 plane Vs of bombers. Soon his squadron settled above and forward of the 16 B-25s and the 12 B-17s. The 35th Fighter Group commander called his pilots. "The Forts will be going in first to hit the runways. You'll have to make a special effort today. Those Nips will be mad as hell when these B-17s chop up the runways and those Mitchells come in at low level heights."

A silence now reigned over Port Moresby until 1340 hours when another burst of aircraft engines echoed across the sprawling Allied base. This time the whines came again from 12 Mile Drome. Sixteen P-39s under Maj. George Welch of the 8th Group's 35th Squadron moved slowly up the taxiways. The men here, watching these planes take off, stared curiously at the honeycombs under the P-39 wings with the countless white balls—"parafrags.

"Weird, ain't they?" one of the 35th Squadron ground crewmen said.

"If it gets the job done, who cares," a burly sergeant answered.

"You think Major Welch and his boys have practiced enough with those things?" the first man asked. "Christ, they've only tried them two or three times."

"They'll be all right. Anyway, they're not going too far."

True. Maj. George Welch's 16 Airacobras would make the relatively easy strike at Ioribaiwa, hoping to further tear apart the Japanese positions of Gen. Tomitaro Horii's Nankai Shitai Detachment. According to Papuan scouts, the low level A-20 attack of 20 September had caused considerable damage, not to mention the consternation among the Japanese ground units. Welch hoped to bring more distress today with several parafrag and strafing runs.

By 1350 hours, a strange quiet descended over Moresby. All the aircraft were gone. The men left behind felt an apprehension for the countless combat airmen flying over the Owen Stanleys. If they met Zeros — could they handle the superior enemy fighter planes and their experienced pilots? How many of these American and Australian pilots would come back? As the ground crews of these various Allied air units returned to their campsites, few of them really believed the American and Australian air armadas would surprise the Japanese. No, there would be interdiction by Japanese fighter planes and heavy ack-ack fire.

And worse, suppose the Japanese were planning an equal surprise attack today? If they came over Moresby, they could destroy every runway on the base, for they would have only ack-ack gunners to challenge them.

Americans and Australians alike could only conjecture. Still, they clearly understood one thing on this muggy, cloudy September afternoon. Every man in Moresby and even the Aussie Diggers at Imita Ridge recognized the significance of this afternoon. The 5th Air Force had sent out almost every available aircraft on five simultaneous missions. If the Allied airmen failed, if the Japanese decimated the Allied bombers with Zero fighter planes, Port Moresby would be totally exposed.

CHAPTER TWELVE

At the Japanese air base in Gasmata on New Britain's southern coast, Lt. Toshio Handa walked leisurely along the runway with Lt. Cmdr. Tadashi Nakajima at his side. At 1300 hours on this 22 September day, both men felt perspiration prickling their necks, foreheads and arms. Despite the cloudiness all day, the humidity was high, drawing sweat from everyone here, albeit Gasmata was on the coast of the Solomon Sea. As the two squadron leaders strolled slowly about the runway, enlisted men were making rechecks on the big Betty bombers that had come from Arawe and now sat wing tip to wing tip along the runway. The ground crews swarmed in and around the G-M 4s like busy bees swarming in and out of a hive. For want of anything to do, while they waited for the weather to clear, they simply made repeat inspections of electrical systems, mechanical gear, engines, and ordnance equipment. These ground crews worked with a hint of disgust, for they had already checked and rechecked the aircraft.

The enlisted men, when they saw the two officers, quickly stiffened to attention, whether on a fuselage of an aircraft, on a wing, inside a Betty cabin, or even from a ladder that reached up to the twin engines. Lieutenant Handa merely gestured the ground crews at ease and the men resumed their work.

"How many aircraft did you bring, Tadashi?" Handa asked.

"Twenty-six Mitsubishis," Nakajima answered, "our entire 11 Squadron." He suddenly squeezed his face. "We lost four aircraft on our last mission to Guadalcanal. I am not so certain that our Zeros are superior to the Yankee aircraft of the American navy."

"I have heard that the war goes very hard in the Solomons," Handa said.

"Difficult indeed," Nakajima nodded. "There is no progress on either side. Our 17th Army troops have been unable to dislodge the American marines from Guadalcanal. But the enemy has not been able to stop our reinforcements, either, for our navy is quite superior to the American navy."

"And the air war?" Handa asked.

"The air war in the Solomons has been quite discouraging," Nakajima said. "We lose too many aircraft by flying all the way from Rabaul to the battle zones in the Solomons. Our fighter pilots and our bomber crews are spent from the long flight from Rabaul, while the Americans need only rise from their airfield on Guadalcanal. But we are told that our engineers are building a new field at Buin in Bougainville and this will cut the distance to Guadalcanal in half."

"That should help," Handa nodded. He stared to his right where Zeros were also lined up wing tip to wing tip, and where other ground crews were working on these same fighter planes, also like busy bees. Here, too, the mechanics and ordnance men stiffened to attention as the two officers approached. But they too reverted to their work when Handa or Nakajima gestured to them.

"How long have you been detached from the Tinian Wing?" Handa asked.

"About ten days," Lieutenant Commander Nakajima said. "They called back two squadrons from New Guinea to Rabaul the day after the Americans attacked the Buna resupply ships. I admit, we have found the air battles at Guadalcanal much worse than the air war in New Guinea. The Americans seem to have more aircraft there. Fortunately, I have some excellent pilots in my squadron, pilots like Saburo Sakai and Hiroyashi Nishizawa. Only because of men like them have we suffered minimum losses in the Solomons."

"Well," Lieutenant Handa grinned and tapped Nakajima on the shoulder, "you are now back in the New Guinea campaign, at least temporarily. You and your pilots will again enjoy combat against smaller numbers of inferior P-39s and P-40s. Is that not so?"

"True," Nakajima nodded. "We welcome this change. Have you heard further from Captain Shingo?"

"No. We are still awaiting favorable weather. So far as I know, the original plan still prevails. We will leave Gasmata with our two squadrons of forty-eight Mitsubishi heavy bombers at the same time that Captain Shingo leaves Buna with the two heavy bomber squadrons of A Group. Thus, we will be over Port Moresby about an hour after Captain Shingo to complete the destruction of the enemy's runways."

"I am surprised that you are not in Buna with Captain Shingo. Why is it you have been placed in command of these heavy bomber squadrons from Arawe?"

"I do not know," Handa said. "I believe Captain Shingo wanted someone with experience in bombing raids over Port Moresby to lead this C Group of the 4th Kokutai Bomber Wing."

"I suspect you are on your way to promotion to lieutenant commander," Nakajima grinned.

"Perhaps," Handa said.

Nakajima now shook his head. "I cannot envision nearly a hundred Mitsubishi heavy bombers striking Port Moresby. The destruction from such a force will surely leave an impact our enemies will long remember."

"One hundred fifty bombers, Tadashi, one

hundred fifty," Handa corrected the 11 Squadron leader. "Remember, the Aichi dive bombers of Commander Shimada will also strike Port Moresby. They will attack the parked aircraft just before Captain Shingo makes his high altitude attack with the heavy bombers."

"Amazing," Nakajima shook his head again. "I cannot recall when Japan mounted so many bombers on a single mission."

"Well, the aircraft are ready," Handa said. "We need only await word from Captain Shingo."

At the same 1300 hours, in the grass shack rest hut at Gasmata, P/1c Saburo Sakai and P/1c Hiroyashi Nishizawa sat with other pilots of 11 Squadron and with some of the air crews of 37 and 38 Squadrons that had come from Arawe with their Betty bombers. The men drank juice and nibbled on rice cookies on this sunless, muggy September afternoon. Ever since noon meal, they had been discussing the action in the South and Southwest Pacific areas: New Guinea, New Britain, and the Solomon Islands.

"Have they experienced many air attacks here at Gasmata?" Private Sakai asked one of the 37 Squadron bombardiers.

"Only two, I am told," the bombardier answered, "but I understand the enemy aircraft did only slight damage." The man suddenly grinned. "In fact, it seems safer here than at Rabaul. The Yankee air force has struck Rabaul many times with their heavy aircraft, is that not so"

"Yes," Sakai nodded. "How long has your squadron been at Arawe?"

"Only three weeks," the bombardier said. "But our work has been quite minimal thus far. We have yet to mount any major bombing attack, so we look forward to this heavy strike on Port Moresby."

"You are fortunate that your bombers are not flying sorties to the Solomons. Every day, the Mitsubishi heavy bombers go out and every day they return in reduced numbers. The air war in the Solomons is hell compared to the air war in New Guinea."

"So I have heard," the bombardier said. Then he looked at Private Nishizawa. "Have you too found the air war in the Solomons worse than New Guinea?"

Nishizawa never altered his poker face. "It makes no difference to me whether I shoot down the Yankee dogs over Guadalcanal or over New Guinea."

The bombardier frowned, but Sakai grinned, and he leaned closer to the man. "Nishizawa has shot down countless enemy aircraft in New Guinea and he has already shot down five of the American marine aircraft over Guadalcanal, more than any other fighter pilot in Rabaul."

"You are to be congratulated," the bombardier told the sober faced Nishizawa. "With pilots like you to escort our heavy bombers to Port Moresby, we can feel safe over the enemy stronghold."

P/1c Hiroyashi Nishizawa only grunted.

"Your comrade is not very friendly, is he?" the bombardier asked Sakai.

"No, but in the air he is The Devil."

"The devil!" the navigator's eyes suddenly brightened. He then looked in awe at Nishizawa. "Am I sitting in the presence of the legendary Devil himself? The scourge of Allied airmen?"

Nishizawa did not even react. He merely took another sip of his juice, leaving to Saburo Sakai the task of answering the Betty bomber crewman. "You are indeed in the presence of The Devil," Sakai said. "When we leave for this mission to Port Moresby, you will see with your own eyes the Devil at his best."

"I shall look forward to this spectacle," the bombardier said. He then looked out of the open hut window at the low, gloomy clouds. "With this weather, I do not know if we shall ever make the sortie to Port Moresby."

"We will make the sortie," Sakai said. "The weather always changes sooner or later. Meanwhile, we may as well enjoy this period of leisure."

"True," the navigator nodded. "We should take advantage of this respite."

Hiroyashi Nishizawa said nothing. He merely sat quietly and soberly, sipping more of his juice.

In their complacency here at Gasmata, not Lieutenant Handa, not Nakajima, not the Betty bombardier, Sakai, or even Nishizawa realized a sobering fact: 24 B-26s under escort of 30 of the new P-38s had just crossed the Papuan coast and were now droning across the Solomon Sea toward Gasmata.

At Buna, across the Solomon Sea, the Japanese had not detected the American air armada heading for Gasmata for the 22nd Group had crossed the coast far to the north of Buna, halfway between this base and the Japanese base at Salamaua. Thus, at this same 1300 hours, Capt. Uehara Shingo and Cmdr. Bunji Shimada sat leisurely in Shimada's quarters. They had just finished their noon day meal of fish, rice, saki, and tea. The two air commanders looked at some maps, while Captain Shingo ran his finger on a line between Buna and Moresby.

"We will follow the usual route to the enemy stronghold to avoid their warning stations in the Owen Stanleys."

"Do they still maintain these stations?" Commander Shimada asked. "Do we not control the Owen Stanley trails almost into Port Moresby itself?"

Captain Shingo grinned. "The Australians are clever. They have simply moved deeper into the jungle and the Nankai Shitai cannot possibly comb every yard of the jungle hills of the Owen Stanley Mountains." He touched the map again. "This will be the safest route, and we will fly as low as possible to avoid the Australian warning units."

Shimada nodded. He then squinted at the sunless day beyond his quarters. "I am getting restless as are my crews. I wish we could fly out now on this sortie to Port Moresby."

"My own heavy bomber crews are also restless," Shingo said, "but we have no control over the weather. We must simply wait."

"This strike will indeed be our greatest attack thus far against the enemy at Port Moresby. I cannot even conceive of such a massive attack," Shimada shook his head. "One hundred fifty bombers."

"Perhaps we should have struck with one hundred fifty bombers last month," Captain Shingo gestured. "If we had, our enemies at Port Moresby might still be repairing runways."

"Captain," Shimada said, what of this new technique by the Americans at our base in Ioribaiwa — this parachute bomb? Do you believe the tactic will be a serious threat to us?"

"No," Captain Shingo shook his head. "I'm sure the tactic was born from desperation. As soon as we clearly understand this new tactic, we will make adjustments in both anti-aircraft and fighter interception techniques to deal with it. I have learned that the Honorable Horii has already taken steps at Ioribaiwa to deal with this parachute bomb. He intends to build deeper bunkers with log covers and packed dirt over the logs. The enemy can make a direct hit with this small bomb and such a hit will cause little damage to such strong bunkers."

"But what of aircraft? Can such low level bombing techniques perhaps cause extensive damage to our aircraft? We keep many aircraft hidden under trees, but at such a low level, cannot the enemy detect them and perhaps destroy them?"

"I would not concern myself with this worry," Captain Shingo gestured. "If we are successful in these planned strikes, the enemy will have no runways in any case to launch aircraft with their parachute bombs."

Then a messenger came into Commander Shimada's quarters. "Please forgive me, Honorable Commander," the man bowed, "but I have another message from Lae."

"Thank you, Corporal," Cmdr. Bunji Shimada said. The B Goup commander read and then turned to Shingo. "The message is from Captain Saito. He reports that his squadrons at Salamaua will have sixty Mitsubishi fighter planes to escort our Aichi dive bombers to Port Moresby. They only await word from me before they take off to make a rendezvous with our B Group."

"Then we should feel quite satisfied," Capt. Uehara Shingo said. "With over fifty fighter planes to escort our heavy bombers here in Buna, and with a squadron of fighter planes to escort our C Group of heavy bombers in Gasmata, we will have ample escorts to conduct our attack on Moresby." He nodded, mostly to himself. "Every airman in the Tinian and 4th Kokutai Wings has prepared well. When we strike Port Moresby, we will do so with near precision. It will be one of our greatest achievements in this campaign."

"That's because you planned well, Captain, and you were able to convince the Honorable Kasaka to give you the airmen and aircraft you need to carry out these strikes." Shimada looked beyond the paneless window of his quarters at the jammed Betty and Val aircraft lining the Buna runway. "I do have one concern, Captain—all these aircraft exposed along the runway. They represent a most inviting target for an enemy air attack. I wonder if the aircraft should not be scattered or hidden under trees."

"Under normal circumstances, I would say yes," Shingo said. "But not today. All aircraft are grounded, ours as well as the enemy. When the time comes, we will be in the position to strike first, for we will learn first of any weather changes."

Shimada nodded.

Neither Capt. Uehara Shingo nor Cmdr. Bunji Shimada knew that 28 American bombers, under an escort of 24 fighter planes, were droning toward Buna: 12 B-17s and 16 B-25s with a unique adaptation that would shock Americans and Japanese alike.

At Lae, Capt. Masahisa Saito sat in a small grass shack, his Tinian Wing headquarters hut. He scanned some reports on his desk before an aide came inside with a weather report: dense clouds still hanging over the Bismarck Archipelago, but expected to start clearing within the next 24 hours, possibly as early as this afternoon. Saito pursed his lips. Perhaps, by morning, he would be escorting Captain Shingo's bombers to Port Moresby. Saito then looked at a sheet of paper on his desk and nodded to himself. All was in readiness.

The Tinian Wing commander would lead 12 Squadron and Lieutenant Sasai would lead his 10 Squadron, a total of 56 Mitsubishi fighter planes. His fighter plane squadrons at Salamaua would escort Commander Shimada's dive bombers, while the borrowed squadron of fighters from Rabaul would lead the C Group of heavy bombers. Saito would have no fighter planes in reserve in the event of an emergency and he did not like the idea. If any enemy aircraft attacked any of the Papuan air bases while the air armadas were droning to Port Moresby, there would be no Japanese planes to defend these bases. Still, perhaps the opportunity to destroy Port Moresby was worth the gamble.

Captain Saito now left his office and walked into the gloomy, humid afternoon. He wiped the perspiration from his forehead with two fingers and he then walked toward the runway where swarms of fighter planes sat in neat rows along the airstrip. Saito did not like to keep his planes so fully exposed in such great numbers. But his entire Tinian Wing was on alert for immediate take-off — as soon as word came from Buna. In any event, Saito told himself, no Allied planes were likely to make an appearance on such a day as this.

As Saito stood near a line of Mitsubishi fighter planes, he thought again of this new parachute bomb that had so rattled General Horii and that had caused such apparently heavy damage to the Japanese base at Ioribaiwa. Hopefully, once they made this massive air strike on Moresby, General Horii would not suffer a repetition of the para-frag bomb attack.

Then a radio man came up to Captain Saito with a sheet of paper in his hand. "Honorable

Saito, a message from Ioribaiwa."

Captain Saito nodded, took the message, and read the report from General Horii.

"Strange reports have been coming out of Moresby. The Allies seem to be preparing aircraft by the dozens for some apparent air sortie. Port Moresby is closed in with dense clouds as are all other areas of Papua. Yet, a burst of activity has prevailed at the enemy base since mid-day. Vanguard sentinels south of Ioribaiwa have reported hearing a din of aircraft engines, indicating the Allies are preflighting swarms of bombers and fighters on their airfield. Is it possible that the Tinian Wing can send a reconnaissance flight to Port Moresby, even in this inclement weather, to investigate? Signed: Gen. Tomitaro Horii."

Captain Saito stroked his chin, somewhat surprised. He could not believe that Allied air commanders in Moresby would be planning strikes today. Yet the Allies might try anything as they were obviously desperate, since Horii's troops were now ready to overrun Port Moresby. Saito looked at the radio man who had brought him the message.

"Bring Lieutenant Sasai to me at once."

"Yes, Honorable Captain," the radio man bowed before moving off.

Yes, Captain Saito nodded to himself, he would ask Sasai to send out a small recon flight, even in this foul weather. Saito had to know the truth. Were the Allies in Port Moresby ready to take a reckless gamble with their air units? If so, the Japanese must know this. Saito was fully aware that all Japanese air bases in Papua as well as Gasmata were jammed with aircraft at the present moment. The fields were never more vulnerable to an air attack than they were on this overcast day. If by some miracle, Allied air units could cross the mountains today, they could cause disaster to the 24th Air Flotilla.

Saito returned to his office to await Lieutenant Sasai. He would send out a half dozen planes that would still leave him with 50 to escort the bombers of the 4th Kokutai Wing. Unfortunately, the message from General Horii had been quite slow in reaching Captain Saito. At this very moment, 12 Fortresses and 24 Havocs carrying honeycombs of parafrags were less than a half hour from Lae.

If any Japanese commander worried about air attacks, that commander was Gen. Tomitaro Horii. Since the unexpected parafrag strike, Horii had put his men to work non-stop to build deep bunkers with log roofs to thwart any further damage from this new Allied air strategy. But his men at Ioribaiwa could not complete the job at once and by the afternoon of 22 September his troops had only begun the task. But worse, scouts had brought Horii some disheartening news. Besides the heavy 5th Air Force activity in Moresby, scouts now informed Horii that reinforcement Australian combat troops had moved up from Port Moresby to relieve the battered and exhausted Australians at Imita Ridge. The scouts could not determine the size of these reinforcements, but they guessed the fresh units to be of perhaps brigade strength, maybe 2,500 to 3,000 men.

Horii was not too concerned about these new Australian arrivals, but he worried about something else. If a brigade of combat troops had reached the jungle battle area, how long would it be before another brigade or even a division of enemy troops reached Imita Ridge?

Horii knew that he must begin his advance on Moresby as soon as possible, before added reinforcements reached Imita Ridge to stop him. He had already delayed too long while he waited for the Japanese Air Force to make their strike on Moresby. He squinted at the low, thick, dark clouds with a mixture of relief and disdain. The poor weather probably ruled out any new parafrag attacks on his Ioribaiwa positions, but the same inclement weather had also delayed the Japanese air strike on Moresby.

If the Japanese air commanders at Papuan air bases would suffer from Allied air attacks within the next 15 to 20 minutes, time had run out for General Horii. He had barely listened to the scout reports of Australian reinforcements when the sudden drone of aircraft echoed from the south. Then a swarm of planes emerged and Japanese sentinels ran into the partially obscured Ioribaiwa positions.

"Enemy fighter planes! Enemy fighter

planes!"

"Take cover, take cover," Horii shouted.

The Nankai Shitai commander expected the enemy planes to make strafing runs and perhaps drop hundred pound bombs. But he stood near his foxhole in utter shock when he saw the dozens of small parachutes fall from the bellies and wings of the zooming P-39s before the parachutes drifted through the trees and once more exploded in staccato bursts on Horii's positions. Again men died, others suffered wounds, and stacks of supplies went up in fire and smoke. Horii, livid, stood almost totally exposed, shaking his fist at the parafrag assailants. Not until the P-39s of Maj. George Welch's 35th Squadron banked away and came back to make strafing runs did Horii duck into his foxhole.

The sudden aerial attack lasted ten minutes but the sixteen P-39s left a pall of heavy smoke hanging over the Japanese positions. Horii could only curse again. The enemy had struck once more with this new devil tactic—and before Horii could prepare his positions to withstand such attacks with minimum damage.

Less than fifteen minutes after leaving Ioribaiwa, the P-39s were back in Moresby, flying low under the clouds and dipping their wings in a sign of triumph. The men at 12 Mile Drome had been uncertain until the spectators counted 16 planes. All the aircraft had returned.

Fifteen minutes after the 16 planes touched down safely and the flyers reported for post mission briefings, the pilots still wore elated looks on

226

their faces. The P-39s had gone to Ioribaiwa and laid over 500 parafrags on the Japanese positions, erupting dozens of fires and leaving palls of smoke. The Airacobras had then raked the area with heavy strafing fire to erupt more fire and smoke. Finally, the P-39s had released dozens of 37mm cannon shells to cause more damage.

"How bad did you hit them, Major?" an operations captain asked Welch.

"I don't know," the major answered, "but you can't see a green tree top for all the smoke and fire."

"Then you hurt them bad," the captain said.

"All I know — we left the whole goddamn area in smoke and flames," Welch said. "Those parafrags are unreal. We got right on top of them, almost saw their eyeballs before we let loose."

"Jesus," somebody in the 35th Squadron briefing room said, "sixteen planes and you did all that damage?"

"We don't know how much," Welch said again, "but it must have been plenty."

If Welch did not know how badly they had hit the Nankai Shitai positions at Ioribaiwa, General Horii knew the results quite well. He stood aghast, staring in fury at the burning stacks of supplies and equipment under the blackened jungle trees. At his side, Col. Yosuke Yokoyama stood just as awe stricken.

"A disaster, Honorable Horii, a disaster," the colonel said.

"Captain Saito was told of this air activity by

the enemy in Port Moresby," Horii fumed. "Why did he not send out aircraft to check these reports?"

"They are preparing to escort bombers to Moresby," Yokoyama said.

"But they made no strikes," Horii gestured angrily. "They allowed the American pigs to make another of these devil tactic strikes on our position. You will call Lae again at once, Colonel, and tell Captain Saito to send fighter planes over our positions immediately."

"Yes, Honorable Horii," Yokoyama said.

The general shook his head. "Our plans to continue the march have been seriously delayed. We will need to bring up new supplies and swiftly since the enemy is now moving combat troop reinforcements into the fight."

"I will call Lae at once," Yokoyama said, "and then call Kokoda to send new supplies immediately."

Masahisa Saito responded immediately to the Ioribaiwa request for air cover. He ordered the veteran Lt. Junichi Sasai to take his full 10 Squadron immediately to Ioribaiwa, despite the low overcast. "You will stay there until relieved," Saito said, "perhaps in two hours."

"Yes, Honorable Saito."

CHAPTER THIRTEEN

At 1330 hours, Col. John Davies peered from the cabin of his B-25 and stared at the dense clouds that he knew covered the rolling ridges of the rugged peaks of the Owen Stanleys. The mass of forested vegetation that resembled a rumpled green blanket with interspersed green flats were not evident on this gloomy day because of the endless cloud cover. But above the overcast, the afternoon sun was quite bright, a sun almost directly overhead.

Although Davies had made numerous flights over these Owen Stanleys, the colonel felt uneasy, for these mountains and the breathless, scenic landscape of Papua, normally visible on a clear day, represented the final outpost of a prehistoric age. If the colonel needed to parachute into the jungle hills, he knew his chances for survival would be slim indeed.

Davies now searched the open sky for Zeros that too often rose from Lae or Salamaua to meet American and Australian formations over the Owen Stanleys. American or Australian planes rarely flew combat missions in this kind of weather, so Davies hoped that no enemy aircraft appeared on this early afternoon.

The 3rd Group commander looked at the two B-25s on each side of his lead V, Mitchells that hung like dangling spiders in mid-air. He glanced at the map pasted to the dashboard of his cabin and he then studied the instruments: another 20 minutes to Buna. He stared at the B-17s slightly above and ahead of him, the Forts also droning in 3 plane Vs. Finally, he glanced at the P-39s that hung about the bombers in a loose ring. Davies pursed his lips, picked up his intercom and called his turret gunner.

"Sergeant, any sign of Zeros?"

"No sir," Sgt. Elbert Jones answered.

Jones had been in combat longer than he cared to remember. He had been one of the lucky ones to escape the Philippines with big John Davies and others of the old 27th Bomb Group. He had then found himself flying as a gunner on an A-24 in Java. When he reached Australia, he had enjoyed a mere few weeks in Brisbane before shipping up to Chartres Towers to join the recently arrived 3rd Bomb Group. Then he had flown again as an A-24 gunner before flying as a turret gunner on a B-25. Now, like Davies, Jones also feared interceptors or the hostile terrain below.

Davies, meanwhile, straightened in his pilot seat and peered once more at both the B-17s ahead and the P-39s alongside. Some of the Airacobras had gone off from the bombers, arching and turning far ahead to search for possible Japanese interceptors. The 3rd Group colonel looked at his map. Yes; they were almost there. Then he looked at his watch: 1350 — another ten minutes.

A call came from the 43rd Group commander. "All pilots, we will now descend through the clouds. Ceiling expected to be one thousand feet. Please refer to your map and make certain you emerge over the Kumusi River Valley."

"Roger," Col. John Davies answered.

Davies turned to his co-pilot, Ray Wilkins, who merely looked blankly at his commander. Despite the maps and assurances, Wilkins was uneasy. There was no guarantee they would get into the clouds and not strike a mountain peak before emerging into the clear.

The two men stared intently from the cabin of the B-25, watching the B-17s drop like odd shaped balloons before enveloping themselves in the clouds. Davies took a deep breath and began his own descent. Soon, he too was lost in the clouds before both he and Wilkins stiffened in the cabin and stared at the altimeter: 6,000, 5,000, 4,000, 3,000, 2,000. Shudders ran up their spines. The mist suddenly disappeared and down below was the winding abyss that snaked through the wide Waroipi Valley — the Kumusi River. Both men uttered deep sighs and then relaxed.

Davies picked up his radio. "This is Reaper Leader, Reaper Leader to all units. We'll alter course to eleven o'clock for two minutes; then turn ninety degrees and head for target on a .014 bearing. Repeat: eleven o'clock for two minutes and then head for target on a .014 bearing."

The droning aircraft veered in unison, banking left in their still tight V formations. The B-25s then straightened and droned on for two minutes before they began banking into a 90 degree turn before leveling off.

Now in the early afternoon, Davies hung at 1,000 feet above the Kumusi River that wound northeastward like a dark gray serpent. Davies looked again at his map. The chart indicated that Davies had a clear route now over the lowlands that stretched for more than 20 miles in from the Buna coast. He saw the B-17s in front of him, just under the clouds where they would drop their bombs from below 1,000 feet. The colonel picked up his intercom again.

"We'll be dropping to tree top level in one minute; one minute. Be sure you stay in pairs and at least five hundred yards apart. Don't fly any closer or you might catch the bomb explosions ahead."

Col. Donald Hall, flight leader of the 13th Squadron acknowledged the colonel's instructions. "We'll come in behind you, Colonel."

At about 1405 hours, a little more than an hour after leaving Moresby, Col. John Davies roared over the Buna plains that lay below his B-25. Davies looked about him and saw the P-39s of the

35th Fighter Group arching and skittering beyond his bombers like low flying hawks. The escort did not lose him this time. When Davies looked down again, he stared in surprise at the rows of planes, hordes of Betty and Val bombers — all sitting along the Buna runways. Davies had rightly guessed that these planes were in the open because they apparently intended to make another strike at Moresby when the weather cleared. And since the Japanese did not believe the Americans would take off in these thick clouds, they had not hidden their planes.

Davies called his pilots. "We're in luck. They've got plenty of planes down there. We'll circle and come in low from the north, but not until the heavies get in. Those B-17s should be coming in just about now."

Davies roared over the valley and out to sea, the other B-25s following him. The Japanese had expressed surprise when they saw the Mitchells emerge from the north under the low clouds and then go out to sea, north. They could not believe these medium bombers would be flying so low. Perhaps the Mitchells were going up the coast to attack barges. Both Capt. Uehara Shingo and Cmdr. Bunji Shimada burst out of the commander's headquarters hut when they heard the sound of planes. They got outside just soon enough to catch a glimpse of the B-25s going out to sea.

"I do not understand," Captain Shingo said. "Where would these medium bombers go at such low level? They could not possibly attack from such a height."

Commander Shimada shook his head. "I cannot believe they flew all the way from Port Moresby in such weather. How could they do this without striking some of the mountain peaks?"

"They no doubt flew above the clouds and descended when they reached the Wairopi Valley," Shingo said. "Still, it was a dangerous undertaking."

Suddenly an aide ran up to Shimada. "Honorable Commander, the coastal sentinels report the Yankee bombers flying in a northwesterly direction."

Shingo nodded. "As I suspected, they are on the way to Salamaua to attack barges there." Then he shrugged. "They will cause little harm. Come, Bunji, we will return to your headquarters and check again our maps."

But Shimada stroked his chin. "I would like to call Salamaua, Captain. First, we should warn them of these American bombers. I would also ask that they send out a squadron of Mitsubishi fighter planes to intercept these enemy aircraft, whatever their mission."

"That is a wise observation," Shingo said. "We will do so."

But suddenly, the harsh drone of big aircraft came from the south. Six B-17s of the 43rd Bomb Group, barely under the clouds at 1,000 feet, came droning over Buna. Moments later, thousand pound bombs, dozens of them, came sailing into the main Buna runway. The explosions shattered the ground like a series of small earthquakes, ripping huge craters on the airstrip. The B-17s were gone in moments, leaving countless deep craters on the runway.

However the B-17s were not finished. The next wave of Fortresses, six of them, also unloosed dozens of thousand pound bombs from their bomb bays. The B-17s came over in pairs, some 15 seconds apart to drop their loads and erupt more earth shattering explosions on the main and secondary runways. More huge clods of earth spewed from the airstrips. After each Fort dropped six huge explosives, the B-17 roared upward and ducked into the clouds to avoid any damage from the concussioning blasts. By the time these last six Forts had left Buna, the runways had been obliterated. The Japanese would not drive a vehicle over the strips, much less an aircraft.

Shingo and Shimada stood outside the headquarters hut — aghast. They could not accept B-17s coming in this low to make such a run with such heavy bombs — and in such inclement weather.

"I do not believe," Shingo screamed. The 4th Kokutai Wing commander could also see some smoke and fire amidst some of the parked aircraft that had caught shrapnel from the exploding thousand pounders. He stopped a line mechanic who was running past him. "How bad is the damage, how bad?" he asked anxiously.

"The runways are in ruins, Honorable Shingo, total ruins."

"And our aircraft?"

"We were fortunate. Only a few planes were damaged, although some beyond repair."

"That is a consolation," Commander Shimada sighed.

"We will call Lae again," Shingo said, "and ask Captain Saito to send a squadron of fighter planes after these Yankee dogs. I want all of those American bombers shot down before they return to Port Moresby."

"Yes, Captain," Commander Shimada said.

The 4th Kokutai Wing commander had been so intent on the B-17s that he had forgotten the B-25s that had zoomed past Buna and out to sea moments earlier. However, the B-25s had now made their turn and Davies was leading the Mitchells back toward Buna. Even the experienced 3rd Group commander felt needles in his spine and butterflies in his stomach as he crossed the Buna coast at the mouth of the Kumusi River, ten miles north of the Buna airstrips. He stared at the big strafing guns, six of them, jutting from the nose of the Mitchell. Then he squinted from his pilot's seat at the two other .50 caliber guns welded to the fuselage. He ran his tongue around his lips and then looked at his co-pilot.

Young Ray Wilkins only looked back at his commander, not speaking. Wilkins felt the same anxiety as Davies. Yes, they had tested these ten big guns in the front of a B-25, and yes, the adaptations had seemed to work. But now they were flying in combat. Wilkins stared down at the tree tops that whizzed by him as the Mitchell roared southeastward at 250 MPH. And suddenly,

Wilkins jerked when he heard the anti-aircraft fire in the distance. At this low level, such fire could reach up and blow them apart as they came over target. Wilkins nervously licked his lips. He could not guess that the Japanese at Buna had been totally unaware of the approaching Mitchells; that the anti-aircraft fire had been aimed at the retiring B-17s that had ducked into the clouds.

In the top turret, Sgt. Elbert Jones also sat stiffly. The gunner looked anxiously above him for signs of enemy planes but saw only the cover of dark clouds racing across the sky. He too then looked at the trees under him, juts of ragged green peaks that swished past him, He bit his lip, hard, and stared at the twin .50 caliber guns welded on either side of the fuselage. Jones could also visualize the six similar guns pointing out of the Mitchell's nose. He was utterly uncertain, fearing the vibration from ten guns might so badly shudder the plane that his aircraft might simply bounce into the trees, crash, and then explode. The gunner's eyes widened when he saw the smoldering runway and the endless planes lining both sides of the shattered airstrips. He felt Davies alter course to begin his run over the line of aircraft.

Davies himself, along with Ray Wilkins peered at the jammed line of planes ahead of him, never recalling a more inviting target. Davies picked up his radio and called Capt. Don Hall. "This is Reaper Leader to 13 Reaper."

"I read you," Captain Hall answered.

237

"We'll take the aircraft on the north side of the runway, to the left. You can take your squadron over the aircraft on the south side of the runway."

"Roger," Hall answered.

"And be careful. Stay in pairs and stay at least fifteen seconds apart."

Now, big John Davies took a deep breath and put his finger on the bomb release buttons. Lt. Ray Wilkins looked on anxiously as the co-pilot felt his heart pound. Would it really work? Ten fifties blasting away at this low level? Would they catch the shrapnel from the parafrags at this same low level? Might the plane jump and recoil so badly that they would uncontrollably crash?

On the ground, the Japanese were still trying to recover from the shock of the low level B-17 attack. They had almost relaxed and gone about their business of cleaning up after the Fortress strikes when the roar of aircraft now came from the north, very low, as though flying right through the trees. The Japanese stiffened and then gaped when they saw the first V of B-25s, Davies lead flight, roaring over Buna; so low the Japanese could almost see the pilots and co-pilots in the B-25 cabins.

The Japanese stood rigid for a moment and then stared at the array of countless small parachutes that tumbled out of the B-25 bellies like huge, descending snowflakes. And then, a staccato of explosions shook the airfield as frag bombs turned the secondary runway into a punchboard of exploding planes. The stunned Japanese ran in a dozen directions in numbing surprise. They looked in awe as B-25 after B-25 came over Buna, dropping masses of white parachutes at near ground level. The countless explosions destroyed workships, the control tower, and dozens of aircraft that belched fire and smoke. Some of the Mitchells had loosened parafrags on hidden aircraft under the trees, Vals that the pilots of the B-25s could see quite clearly from their low level height. More smoke and fire erupted from the dense jungle brakes.

When the last Mitchell roared away, smoke and fire enveloped the Buna airfield. The low level attack had made the assault extremely accurate and the B-25 pilots had made almost every one of their hundreds of parafrags count positively.

The Japanese might have come out of their shelters to survey the damage, but the Mitchells now returned again at low level. This time, they sprayed streams of heavy incendiary strafing fire about the base: accurate .50 caliber tracers, an unheard of stream from ten guns on each Mitchell. The heavy strafing fire blew up more vehicles, ignited more fires, and burned more of the parked aircraft and the Vals hidden under trees. The Buna airfield, a raging inferno now, lay in near shambles. Every Val and Betty at Buna had been destroyed or damaged.

Col. Richard Legg of the 35th Group's 41st Squadron had been zooming and darting his P-39 under the clouds, as had the other pilots of his fighter squadron. They stared in awe at the devastation about Buna. The parachute bombs had fallen like huge hailstones to leave no Japanese plane untouched. And the fighter pilots found even more uncanny the rattling, shattering echoes of ten .50 caliber guns spewing deadly incendiary fire into the same lines of parked Bettys and Vals as well as the hidden Vals.

When Davies and his pilots made their final runs over the battered base at Buna, the 3rd Group commander called Dick Legg. "Did you find any interceptors, Colonel?"

"Nothing; not a one."

"What about the Fortresses?"

"They're on the way home and I've sent a half dozen P-39s with them. If they run into interceptors, they'll call me and we'll join them. But I don't think they'll see any."

"The nearest interceptors have to be one hundred fifty miles away up at Salamaua," Davies said, "just like we figured. Okay, Colonel, you can bring your boys down and take a few punches yourself."

"You and the heavies didn't leave us much," Legg said, "but we'll get in our licks."

After the last B-25 zoomed up and into the clouds, Col. Richard Legg came down at low level on heavy strafing runs with his remaining ten Airacobras. The American fighter pilots aimed their tracers at any building, vehicle, or aircraft that was not already smashed, burning, or smoking. The 8th Fighter Group pilots now simply completed the job of levelling the Buna airbase.

When the last P-39 droned out of Buna, the Japanese stared dumbfoundedly at the lethal destruction about them. They were not so amazed by the P-39 strafing runs, or even by the low level attack by the B-17s. But the B-25s had stunned the Japanese with their deadly destruction. Unbelievable! Medium bombers dropping hundreds of parafrags at such a low level and then blasting away with more strafing guns than those on a destroyer. The Japanese would need at least a week to repair Buna so they could again base Vals and stage Bettys from here.

As the 16 Mitchells and their escorts droned homeward over the Owen Stanleys, a strange silence prevailed among the airmen. They could not fathom the destruction they had caused with this new, low level parafrag bombing attack and the heavy incendiary strafing assaults. Not an airman on this Buna strike doubted that Pappy Gunn's new technique with the B-25 would turn around the Papuan war. Lt. Ray Wilkins looked at John Davies.

"Jesus, Colonel, I don't believe this."

"Believe it, Lieutenant," Davies answered. "These tactics are the future in this jungle war. Pappy wa right; he's always right." Davies now called his gunner. "Sergeant, do you see anything?"

"No sir," Elbert Jones answered, "just the P-39s above us."

"Stay alert."

"Yes sir," the gunner said again. The disbelief was still cemented on the young gunner's face. He was still numbed by the results of this low level strike by medium bombers. But then, if you got right on top of target, how could you miss?

Col. Dick Legg and his P-39 pilots had caught up to the B-25s some 50 miles south of Buna. Now the 35th Fighter Group commander stared at the six strafing guns that jutted from the noses and the welded .50s that protruded from the fuselages of the B-25s. The colonel could not fathom what he had seen at Buna, a new technique that worked with murderous efficiency. Other pilots of the 8th Group also stared in awe at the B-25s, equally impressed by the work of these converted B-25s. Some also stared at the bellies of the Mitchells from whence had come the awesome parafrags, like some white plague from an alien planet.

These fighter pilots had heard all the rumors, all the reports, all the praise about these new secret weapons that Mad Professor Pappy Gunn had inserted in B-25s and A-20s. They had listened with only minor interest and even some skepticism, for the 5th Air Force was always claiming they had something new that would make a difference in the disheartening air war over New Guinea. But now, they had seen the truth of this latest adaptation. Every fighter pilot in these formations flying back to Moresby, as well as every crew member aboard the B-25s, knew that after today the air war in New Guinea had changed.

Now, Col. John Davies called Richard Legg. "Colonel, have you seen any signs of Zeros?" Davies knew full well there were no Zeros in the area, for he could see as plainly as Legg in the clear skies above the clouds. He had made the call to break the monotony of silence that had muted most of the men in these formations after the astonishment at Buna with parafrags and heavy strafing guns.

"Nothing, Johnny, nothing," Colonel Legg answered.

"Tell your boys to stay alert."

"They'll stay alert." Legg himself now scanned the skies, but he saw nothing.

At Buna itself, Captain Shingo and Commander Shimada stared intently at the destruction about them. No more runways, not one plane undamaged or not destroyed. Not one vehicle still operable and not an undamaged structure. Neither man said anything. What could they say? Even the aides who had surveyed the damage and then came to the headquarters hut, itself slightly damaged, said nothing to the air commanders. They could report nothing that Shingo and Shimada had not seen themselves.

Finally, one brave lieutenant spoke to the 4th Kokutai Wing commander. "Honorable Captain, what is your wish?"

The captain glared at his subordinate and answered angrily. "Call Lae! Tell Captain Saito he must destroy these devil bombers; they must be destroyed!"

"We have already called Lae," the lieutenant answered.

"Well call them again," Shingo barked.

"Yes, Honorable Shingo," the subordinate bowed before he moved away.

243

Then, Capt. Uehara Shingo stared once more at the palls of smoke and belching fire that had once been their proud new airbase at Buna. He gritted his teeth. No planes would fly from Buna for some time. The 4th Kokutai Wing commander only hoped he could still get his Betty bombers in Gasmata out on a strike against Port Moresby before the Allied air forces caused any more damage. He moved angrily away, about to go into the headquarters hut, but stopped suddenly — he needed to wait until service troops had cleared away some of the rubble.

Shingo started to move off in another direction when a radio man came up to him. "Honorable Captain, the latest meteorological reports from Rabaul," he handed the captain the sheet of paper. "They say the weather will clear by tomorrow and may even begin clearing this afternoon."

Shingo stared hard at the radioman, his dark eyes aflame with frustrated anger. He then yanked the sheet of paper from the subordinate, looked up at the clouds, and then crumpled the paper in his hand before throwing the sheet away.

CHAPTER FOURTEEN

At Lae, Capt. Masahisa Saito listened in astonishment to the complaints from the 4th Kokutai Wing commander in Buna as Saito had earlier heard the complaints from Ioribaiwa: medium bombers flying over the airfield at treetop height and leaving utter destruction behind. Fiendish warfare, Captain Shingo had called the strategy. Shingo's ranting laments prompted Captain Saito to act. He suspected that if Allied planes were out this afternoon to hit Buna and Ioribaiwa under low hanging clouds, they might do the same thing to Lae. He ordered the pilots of 12 Squadron to fly off at once and to hover above and under the clouds to forestall any possible attack on Lae.

But only half the squadron, 14 Zeros, became airborne before the drones of B-17 bombers from the south were picked up by inland warning crews who relayed the information to Lae. Saito hurried out of his headquarters just in time to hear the scream of air raid sirens. He grabbed a scurrying airman. "What has happened?"

"Aircraft, far above the clouds, are approaching the Markham Valley."

"At once, tell the airborne pilots to intercept these enemy aircraft."

"Yes, Honorable Saito."

Meanwhile, the B-17s of the 19th Bomb Group and the A-20s of the 3rd Bomb Group came ever closer to Lae. During the flight over the Owen Stanleys, high above the clouds, Bent Nose Whitehead had looked at the strange A-20s with the same curiosity as other pilots in the escorting 80th Fighter Squadron. Whitehead had flown for many years, but he had never seen a light bomber with so many guns jutting from the nose. Nor had Whitehead ever seen in the air an A-20 with a seemingly huge insect hive hanging from the wings or fuselage. The 5th Air Force ADVON commander simply stared at the countless white domes in the honeycombs. And now, as the American air units cleared the last peak before descending to the Markham Valley and flying to their Lae target, Whitehead himself felt a measure of uncertainty. Any moment, he expected Zeros to emerge from the clouds like demons coming out of a soft white mist.

The ADVON commander was about to call somebody about making their drop through the clouds when he heard the call from the

B-17 leader.

"We're approaching target," Col. Dick Carmichael said from his lead Fort. "Maintain 1.6 bearing. We'll descend in one minute and we should emerge over the Markham Valley, about twenty miles from Lae. We'll go in first with the heavies to attack the runways. Light bombers will then follow at treetop level. Escorts will split, maintaining cover above the clouds and below the overcast. Repeat: we descend in one minute; maintain your 1.6 bearing."

General Whitehead, Col. Boyd Wagner, and Maj. Bob Strickland of the 3rd Bomb Group merely listened to instructions. Rank notwithstanding, Colonel Carmichael, leading the B-17s, was in charge of the mission. The 5th ADVON commander would merely follow orders from the formation leader.

Soon, the 12 B-17s and the 24 A-20s dropped into the clouds and fell slowly downward. In the cockpit of his Havoc, Bob Strickland felt a slight chill. He was not certain he could succeed again as he had succeeded at Ioribaiwa. What if Zeros were waiting for them below the clouds. The A-20s and B-17s would be extremely vulnerable at such a low level. Strickland looked at the six big guns jutting from the nose of his lead Havoc and he licked his lips. He squinted from his cabin window to see only the hazy shapes of other A-20s in his lead V. At least they were maintaining their positions in this mist. Then, he called his gunner.

"Sergeant, do you see anybody too close to us?"

"No sir," the gunner answered.

"Stay alert. When we make our run you can strafe on the upturn."

"Yes sir," the gunner said. The sergeant too tightened his face, for he too was not certain the parafrag-strafing attack would work. He nervously fingered the triggers of his twin .50s and then he shuddered. The descent through the clouds seemed never ending. Even though they had been inside the thick mists less than a minute, the time seemed endless. The gunner opened his eyes, stealing a peek, but his heart sank. Dense mists were still all around him.

Far ahead, Col. Dick Carmichael felt an equal uncertainty as he too descended through the clouds for what seemed liked endless minutes. He looked beyond the cabin window at the B-17 hanging next to him, grateful that his Fortress wingman was still in formation. Then Carmichael turned to his co-pilot who was staring intently into the blind mist above, below and around him. The Fort co-pilot felt a sense of panic, as though he was buried in a huge sealed tomb with no means of escape. He looked at the altimeter: 2500 feet. Then, the co-pilot took a deep breath. If they did not come out soon . . . he hoped that Carmichael would pick up his radio and call this whole thing off.

But despite the building fear and tension, Col. Dick Carmichael continued the descent.

Beyond the bombers, the P-39s also descended, and Col. Boyd Buzz Wagner could see General Whitehead's plane at his side in the thick mist. Wagner could also see the obscure black shadows to his right — the descending B-17s. Wagner too was not sure they could come out of the clouds before the Japanese at Lae had Zeros waiting for them. He looked at his altimeter: 2500 feet. If they did not come out soon . . . Buzz Wagner squinted hard to his left, trying to see the face of Whitehead through the mist, trying to determine if Bent Nose felt the same nervousness as Wagner did. But the 8th Group colonel could only see the blurred outline of the general's P-39.

Wagner was tempted to pick up his radio and call Colonel Carmichael, but he suddenly remembered that radio silence would prevail as soon as they dropped into the clouds. For a fleeting moment, Wagner wished he had stayed upstairs, above the clouds, with the ten aircraft he had left behind. But then, the idea suddenly brought on guilt. He knew he belonged here, making the descent through the clouds.

The 8th Group commander knew that the big bombers would go in first, droning over the Lae runway at perhaps less than a thousand feet to drop their heavy thousand pound bombs. If the B-17s did not do enough damage, they would at least cause enough confusion and disruption to force the Japanese to seek cover. Then, hopefully, the A-20s could come in at tree top level to totally surprise the Japanese.

At Lae itself, Capt. Masahisa Saito watched the other pilots of 12 Squadron hurry toward their aircraft, Zeros that lined the runway with engines screaming. Ground crew had ignited engines to preflight the aircraft as soon as the other Zeros of 12 Squadron had taken off. The Tinian Wing commander squinted up at the dark clouds overhead, straining to hear the engines of enemy aircraft that were supposedly approaching Lae in this inclement weather. But he heard nothing. Perhaps the reports were false, especially since Saito had heard nothing from the 14 Zeros of 12 Squadron that had taken off earlier. Saito ambled toward the runway to watch his pilots scoot toward their fighter planes. The pilots would follow the usual course, spreading out in three plane Vs, to cover the air route southeast over the Markham Valley, the route Allied planes generally followed from Port Moresby to make attacks on Lae.

Captain Saito turned to an aide. "Call Lieutenant Tasake at Salamaua. Tell him to send 14 Squadron to Lae and to get his 15 Squadron airborne in the event enemy aircraft attempt to attack Salamaua as they did Buna."

"Yes, Honorable Saito," the aide said before moving off.

Ironically, the 14 Zeros that had already taken off from Lae missed the B-17s and A-20s. At the moment, while the Americans descended through the clouds, the 14 airborne Zeros were rising through the clouds and they came out above the American intruders. They would, however, meet the ten P-39s that Boyd Wagner had left above the clouds.

Finally, at 1410 hours, the American B-17s and A-20s came out of the clouds to see the wide expanse of the Markham Valley below them. Now the American planes droned swiftly northwest. Colonel Carmichael reached Lae first, keeping his B-17 just under the clouds at 900 feet along with his wingman. When the first pair of Forts came over Lae, they dropped screaming thousand pounders that chopped huge craters in one of the runways and set fire to a repair shop. The same bomb drop destroyed four of five Zero fighter planes. Surprisingly, the low bomb drop had enabled the B-17 bombardiers to hit with more than average accuracy. When the first two Fortresses were gone, the next ten followed to thoroughly saturate the runways with craters. The Forts also left palls of smoke. No aircraft would get off the runways.

If the Japanese hoped to still get off their 14 remaining planes of 12 Squadron, such hopes vanished when the A-20s emerged from the trees and roared across Lae. The Japanese watched curiously as descending parafrags drifted over the base before exploding in a staccato of bursts. The low level attack had enabled the A-20 pilots to see the silvery shapes of aircraft so large they could almost reach down and touch them. Not only did aircraft explode, but buildings burned and vehicles belched fire.

"I do not believe!" Saito screamed. "Call the airborne Mitsubishis of 12 Squadron at once. They must return immediately to attack these American bombers."

But Col. Boyd Wagner had quickly seen that no Zeros would attack the American bombers under the clouds. He had also seen that only a dozen or so Zeros were here and he suspected that flocks of Zeros were airborne and somewhere above the clouds. Panic gripped him for a moment. There could be two full squadrons of Zeros aloft, as many as 60 planes. He cried into his radio.

"All pilots! We're going upstairs. There may be a swarm of Nip fighters up there and we can't let them come down here after the bombers."

Then Buzz Wagner zoomed upward, 14 P-39s following him. When he emerged above the clouds a few moments later, he could see in the distance an aerial engagement between his other ten Airacobras and Japanese Zeros. "Let's go," Wagner cried. "They need help."

This time, the American fighter pilots fought with determination. They waded into the Zeros aggressively. Perhaps the 12 Squadron Japanese pilots were squeamish because they were outnumbered, or perhaps the pilots were not sure of themselves. In any event, in the five minute dogfight, Wagner and his 14 pilots shot down six Zeros to a loss of two P-39s. But more important, not a single Zero got near the B-17s or A-20s that were chewing up the Lae airdrome.

Meanwhile, Wagner's other ten P-39 pilots, those who had remained aloft, had knocked five more Zeros out of the air, while the Japanese had not damaged a single P-39. The four remaining Zeros, all that survived the dogfights, simply scooted northward, out of harm's way. This quartet of pilots from the decimated flights from 12

Squadron tried to return to Lae. But the Zero pilots saw only devastation on their airbase when they came out of the clouds. Perhaps they should have attacked the A-20s in the process of chewing up the base with parafrags. But, they were only four and perhaps the swarms of American fighter planes might come out of the clouds and finish off even this quartet of survivors.

One of the Zero pilots called Captain Saito.

"What shall we do, Honorable Commander?"

"You have no choice but to fly to Madang," Saito said, "and pray that you have enough fuel to get there."

So the four Zeros jelled into a tight diamond, turned north, and flew toward Madang, 150 miles to the north.

Captain Saito now called Lieutenant Sasai, whose 10 Squadron was droning toward Ioribaiwa. "Lieutenant, we have suffered an unfortunate air strike at Lae and the runways are inoperable. You cannot return here, nor to Buna. You must abort your mission and fly to Madang before you run out of fuel."

"Yes, Captain," Lt. Junicki Sasai answered.

The American crews and pilots of the Lae strike, meanwhile, rode back to Moresby with the same awe as those on the Buna strike. They could not believe the destruction at Lae. Further, the A-20 and B-17 crews now felt a new respect for the American pilots who had so neatly handled the Zero fighter planes and kept them away from the bombers.

General Whitehead had been completely enthralled by the destruction caused by his bombers, especially the A-20s with their low level strikes. At the old Port Moresby Hotel, he had heard so often the report of another poor bomb strike, so this eye witness victory today could not help but elate him. He had even made a couple of passes himself at one of the Zeros, but he had not hit anything.

To the southeast, some fifty miles away, A/C Frank Lukis still hung in the sky above the clouds in his lead Beaufort. He looked at the twin engine bombers alongside of him in the first lead V of 22 Squadron, Beauforts carrying two thousand pound bomb loads. Lukis intently studied his map and then looked at the clear skies above the dense clouds. Then he looked at his watch: 1350 hours. The Australian commander did not know it, but at the very moment, the attacks on Lae and Buna were almost in progress. Lukis then looked at his altimeter: 10,000 feet. He would soon reach the north coast of Papua, where he would drop under the clouds before making a 180 degree turn to hit Salamaua from the sea. He was not certain he could succeed with such heavy bomb loads at low level, but he knew he must try.

Frank Lukis also tried to squint back at the 16 Beauforts to the rear, those carrying full honeycombs of frag bombs under their wings. Would they succeed with this new kind of aerial attack as the Yanks insisted they would? The Australian air commander looked once more at his map and he then called into his radio: "All pilots, we're now approaching the coast. We will make descent in one minute; one minute." As if to emphasize the point, Lukis revved the engines of his Beaufort and rose some 25 or 30 feet in altitude.

Around the 32 Beauforts and 12 Mitchells hung the P-40s of 75 Squadron under Lt. Larry Jackson who frequently stared at the Beauforts, sometimes expecting those carrying the heavy bombs to drop into the clouds from the loads. Then, Jackson scanned the wide expanse of blue sky around him, expecting to see Zeros coming at him from any direction. He was not certain he could do much with 26 Kittyhawks against a couple of squadrons of Zeros. Jackson knew, at least two squadrons of Japanese fighters were usually based in Salamaua. The 75 Squadron commander licked his lips and called into his radio.

"Stay close, lads, stay close to the Beaus and Mitchells, and keep a sharp look. If you spot anything, report at once. If any Nip Zeros hit those bombers, they could disintegrate in mid air. Keep a good watch on the Yanks. These new boys are in combat for the first time."

If Lukis and Jackson understood the importance of their mission, so too did Capt. Larry Tanberg. He needed to knock out Salamaua today as the Allied 5th Air Force needed to knock out the other bases on today's list of targets. But for these raw Sunsetter crews, success was imperative. They must prove that their training and patience would pay off in a good air strike.

Commander Lukis, in the lead air formation, called again into his radio. "All right lads, we'll begin descent and now maintain radio silence."

Soon the 72 aircraft of the Australian 22 and 75 Squadron and from the 38th Bomb Group's 71st Squadron dropped into the clouds and downward through the mists. Whether or not the Aussies were good, better, or worse than their American counterparts, they did share one common trait with the 38th Group airmen: they felt the same tenseness and uncertainties as the planes fell through the clouds. Would they come into the clear before they hit the ground or the sea?

But the Allied planes were still in the air when they came out of the overcast, now hanging over the dreary surface of the Solomon Sea. Lukis made his turn for the run over Salamaua. He would follow the briefing plan: 16 Beauforts with a pair of thousand pounders hitting the runway, 16 Beauforts coming in even lower to hit installations and aircraft with parafrags, and then the B-25s on strafing and parafrag runs over parked aircraft. The P-40s would make certain that no Zero fighters interfered with the bombing runs.

At Salamaua itself, Zeros were getting ready to take off after the message from Lae. Lt. Takase had just listened to a second message from Lae in utter astonishment: a devastating attack on the airbase, first by B-17s and then by A-20s that carried the strange new parachute bomb.

"The airbase is in total ruins," the Lae operations officer told Takase. "We have no way to land planes here, and a squadron of Mitsubishi fighter planes has been destroyed. You must mount your squadrons at once, for we can expect that Allied bombers will attack Salamaua as they have struck Lae and Buna."

Lieutenant Takase was just taxiing the first flight of Zeros to the runway when Lukis came over the base and grinned. "Okay, lads, there they are, right out in the open and waiting for bombs. A and B Flights will bomb the runway. C and D flight will strike installations, and the Mitchells will follow with strafing and parafrag runs on parked aircraft."

The Japanese at Salamaua looked upward at the sudden sound of aircraft. They did not see any planes—not until the Beauforts came droning over the runway at 800 feet to drop their thousand pound bombs in shattering concussions that threw up tons of dirt throughout the Salamaua base and left huge craters in the runway. One of the thousand pounders caught two Zeros at the head of the runway and blew both planes and pilots into oblivion. Within moments, the runway was destroyed and some of the parked planes damaged.

Then C and D Flights, 16 Beauforts carrying frag bombs, swooped over the base at treetop level and dropped dozens of parafrags on service and repair buildings as well as on some of the parked aircraft taxiing toward the runway. At this low altitude, the 22 Squadron enjoyed better than average success. Buildings and several planes went up in smoke and fire.

Then came the B-25s with heavy strafing fire before the parafrag drops. Tanberg and his Sunsetter crews totally demolished whatever was left of the airbase, destroying at least a dozen planes and damaging as many more. Japanese scrambled in panic to get away from burning planes, heavy strafing fire, and descending parafrags. The low level Beaufort and B-25 attacks had utterly shocked the Japanese. Not a single Zero got off the ground.

After the air attack, Lukis called Tanberg. "We had a good show, Captain. You and your lads did a fine job on your first time out."

"Yes sir, Commander," Tarberg said, his face beaming.

The other airmen of the 38th Bomb Group were just as elated. They had hoped to make a good impression on their first combat mission, but this stunning success over Salamaua had left them in a state of bliss. Further, they had been astonished by the devastating work by the B-25 Commerce Destroyers.

By the time the last Beaufort, B-25, and Kittyhawk had left Salamaua, the airstrip lay like a cratered punchboard and the grounded Zeros, nearly 60 of them, had been destroyed or damaged. The parafrag bomb had done its job again. A/C Frank Lukis was fully satisfied as was Capt. Larry Tanberg.

While Gen. Ennis Whitehead was completing his multiple strikes on this 22 September afternoon, there was more bad news for the Japanese. The fresh Australian 25 Brigade, the reinforcements reported to General Horii earlier in the day by scouts, were expected to reach Imita Ridge as soon as Allied planes had softened up the Nankai

Shitai positions at Ioribaiwa. The fresh Australian brigade would then pound the Japanese ground positions with 25 pounder cannon before moving up to drive the Japanese from Ioribaiwa. Hopefully, the 25 pound artillery barage would destroy anything left in the Japanese position that had not already been macerated by the aerial parafrag bomb attacks.

But worse for General Horii, more Allied troops were also on the way. Gen. Douglas MacArthur had scrounged every ship he could find as well as C-47 transport planes to carry as many troops of the American 32nd and Australian 7th Divisions as he could to Port Moresby. General Horii, of course, had hoped that the massive Japanese air strikes on the Port Moresby airfields would ground Allied planes and thus allow Japanese air units to also pulverize the disembarkation points in the harbor of Port Moresby. The Nankai Shitai commander did not know yet that the Japanese airbases in New Guinea had suffered as badly or worse than he himself had suffered at Ioribaiwa.

Gen. Basil Morris, the operational commander of the Allied New Guinea Force, had read with delight the reports of the air strikes on Buna, Lae, and Salamaua, as he read with pleasure the arrival of more Allied ground troops. Morris was especially happy with the strike report on the attack on Salamaua.

"Looks like our lads and those new Yanks did a good job," Morris said.

"Yes sir," an aide answered.

"Are those 25 Brigade lads on the way?"

"Yes sir," the aide told the general. "They've just about reached Imita Ridge and they'll start 'itting those Nips at Ioribaiwa with twenty-five pound artillery as soon as the Yank airmen finish with these new parachute bombs."

"Good," Morris nodded. Then he called General MacArthur in Brisbane. "The air lads 'ave done a good job, sir. We got excellent reports on the strikes at Lae and Buna, and now we got the latest report from the strike at Salamaua. If these reports of damage are even 'alf accurate, we'll 'ave a real boon, we will."

"What about Gasmata?" MacArthur asked.

"We don't 'ave a report on the sorties to Gasmata yet, sir, but we'll report as soon as we get one."

"Are they on the way?"

"Yes sir," Morris answered. "5th ADVON is 'oping to 'it Gasmata with the same surprise as the other air units 'it these other Japanese air bases."

"Let me talk to General Whitehead."

" 'E's not 'ere, sir," Morris said. "Went out on one of the strikes, 'e did."

"On one of the strikes?" MacArthur barked. "What the hell's the matter with that man? He should be in his headquarters directing this thing. I'll talk to Kenney about that incorrigible. I'm still getting heat from those B-25s that brazen colonel of his took from Brisbane without proper authorization."

"The general's all right, sir," Morris said. " 'E's

on 'is way back from the Lae strike."

"You have him call Brisbane as soon as he gets back," MacArthur fumed.

"Yes sir," General Morris answered.

When he finished talking to MacArthur, Basil Morris sighed, his ears still ringing. Then he stiffened when he heard the sound of aircraft. "What's going on now?"

"The 35 Squadron from the Yank 8 Group," the aide said. "They're going off to make another of those parachute bomb strikes on Ioribaiwa. They expect to go out all afternoon."

"There won't be much left of that Nip base, will there? Not much for our own 25 Brigade lads with their twenty-five pounders."

"We shouldn't complain, sir."

"No," Morris said. Then the New Guinea Force commander rubbed his chin. "No word yet on the strike to Gasmata?"

"No sir."

"Let me know as soon as you 'ear something."

"Yes sir," the aide answered.

CHAPTER FIFTEEN

At about the time Gen. Basil Morris finished meditating in Port Moresby, the 24 B-26s of the 22nd Bomb Group had come under the clouds and were now skimming over the Solomon Sea toward Gasmata on the south coast of New Britain. In this longest flight of all during the 22 September afternoon strikes, the 30 Lightnings of Capt. Tom Lynch had not caught up to the B-26s until the Marauders had crossed the north coast of Papua and had begun the long flight across the sea. The P-38s did not need auxiliary gas tanks for they had been built for long range bomber escort. So they had filled their wing tubes with 12 27mm shells, a total of 24. Further, their four strafing guns were fully loaded with .50 caliber strafing belts.

All during the long flight over the Owen Stanleys, high above the clouds, Capt. Tom Lynch had enjoyed every moment. He found the Lightning quite easy to handle, and without any strain, despite the heavy shell loads and the big gas tanks. Occasionally, he had looked at the other P-38s in his lead diamond formation that hung like suspended wasps. Thus far, the strange looking aircraft had responded to every claim for their speed and rate of climb.

On several occasions, Lynch had picked up his radio to call other pilots and ask the same questions: "Any problems? Any engine strain? Any trouble in maintaining altitude?"

But always came the same answer: no. On occasions, some of the 35th Group pilots added complimentary comments: "Sweet as a baby carriage." "No sweat." "Easy going." Lynch was satisfied. He felt optimistic. Perhaps the Lightning was the aircraft that would finally overcome the Zero, the plague of Allied airmen during these early months of the Southwest Pacific war. But perhaps they would catch the Bettys and Zeros at Gasmata with the same surprise as other Allied air units had caught the Japanese at Buna, Lae, and Salamaua and there would be no aerial dogfights with enemy fighter planes.

At 1310 hours, while other units were droning toward New Guinea targets, Lynch finally saw his B-26 charges ahead, far above the clouds over the Solomon Sea. The captain brought his P-38s alongside the Marauders, taking his own 39th Squadron to the left of the B-26s and sending Capt. Bob Faurot with the P-38s of the 40th

Squadron to the right side of the droning bombers.

When the Lightnings had settled in their escort patterns, the bomber crews peered at the weird machines with curiosity. They wondered how the tic-tac-toe shaped aircraft stayed aloft, much less flew. The crews had never seen this kind of plane before: twin fuselage, twin engines, twin tails— 30 of them. And soon, at 1315 hours, Col. Dwight Devine cried into his radio.

"All aircraft will now descend through the clouds."

Moments later, 24 Marauders and 30 Lightnings dropped into the clouds to come out a few moments later some 2,000 feet above the Solomon Sea. Both Devine and Lynch were surprised at the high ceiling. The weather front had begun to thin this far north. The American planes droned toward Gasmata. A few of the P-38s remained above the clouds to watch for Zeros up above and three other P-38s shot ahead of the formation to bank and turn in the van to report any enemy planes.

Co-pilot Walter Kell, in the lead plane of the first V of bombers, turned to Colonel Devine. "Jesus, I can't get over those weird looking planes."

Devine shook his head. "They do look like freaks."

"They say the plane climbs like a rocket and goes up to forty thousand feet."

"Christ, that's halfway to the moon," the 22nd Group commander grinned. "I'll have to see it to believe it."

Devine and the others aboard the bombers would indeed see and believe.

The American armada droned on for only another few minutes when suddenly there were no more clouds. They had come abruptly out of the low front and now only clear skies lay ahead. Colonel Devine called into his radio. "A bit of luck, boys; we've hit the start of that clearing trend. We'll rise to five thousand feet and make our runs over the runway from there."

The Marauders rose in altitude, the P-38 escorts rising with them.

But the clearing weather as well as the reports of Allied attacks on New Guinea bases had alerted Lieutenant Handa. The first hint of an expected attack on Gasmata came when a Japanese patrol craft off the coast of Gasmata spotted the American planes 50 miles off the New Britain coast. They radioed Lt. Toshio Handa at once and Handa called immediately on Lt. Cmdr. Tadashi Nakajima. "Enemy aircraft. There is no doubt they intend to strike us here as they have struck in New Guinea."

"We will mount our squadron at once," Nakajima answered. "Fortunately, our aircraft have been fully loaded and ready for the Port Moresby strike. The Americans will not surprise us here today as they did elsewhere."

Within a few minutes, 26 Zeros of the Tinian Wing's 11 Squadron were ready and pilots scrambled into the cockpits. A few minutes later, the Zeros were taking off in pairs down the Gasmata runway. Lieutenant Handa watched the quick, efficient take off. He felt smug. These experienced Zero pilots would make short work of the Yankee airmen.

"We will hang at thirty thousand feet," Lieutenant Commander Nakajima told his pilots. "Such an altitude will place us in good position to swoop down on the enemy bombers. Their fighter escorts cannot deal with us at this height. By 1350 hours, 23 pilots were following Nakajima high into the sky to level off at 30,000 feet.

"Here we wait," Nakajima said.

As the droning American bombers came on, Bob Faurot of the 40th Fighter Squadron got a report from his wingman. "Captain, Zeros up ahead. They're gone upstairs, maybe to twenty-five or thirty thousand feet."

"Bandits ahead," Captain Faurot called Lynch.

"We'll go to forty thousand," Lynch said. "Check your oxygen masks." Then Lynch called the leader of the 39th Squadron. "We've spotted Zeros at twenty-five thousand. We're going upstairs but I'd like you to leave D Flight below with the bombers in case more enemy Zeros try to hit those B-26s low."

"Okay," the flight leader of D Flight answered. "We'll hang close to the bombers. If any of the bastards get through, we'll take care of them. Good luck."

Capt. Tom Lynch arched his plane and whined into a steep climb, looking at his altimeter and stiffening with each rise in the needle: 20,000,

266

25,000, 30,000, 35,000, 40,000. He then leveled off and sighed. When he looked down, a strange miniature world lay under him. He was like an alien who had just come from another planet and who now hovered over planet Earth.

The other P-38 pilots had climbed after Lynch and now the formation of 16 Lightnings droned northward. "Stay in pairs, in pairs; stick to wingmen," Lynch cried into his radio. "Make sure your oxygen masks are okay." Soon, the 39th Squadron commander spotted the Zeros under him. "Okay, let's scramble!"

Suddenly, the whine of P-38 engines exploded across the high sky as the Lightnings dove downward like shooting meteors. Tadashi Nakajima suddenly jerked when he heard the whines above, and he looked up in utter astonishment to see the strange, twin engine aircraft zooming downward. The Japanese squadron leader could not digest the sight. How could any plane fly above the high level Zero? Nakajima picked up his radio and cried frantically to his other pilots.

"Enemy fighter planes! Enemy planes from above us!"

The other Zero pilots stared up in shock.

"We must avoid them and attack the Yankee bombers," Nakajima cried. Then, he opened the throttle and shot southward, the other Zeros followed him.

The Zeros could not outdive or outrun the P-38s. Capt. Tom Lynch and Capt. Bob Faurot quickly caught up to the four flight diamonds of tail end Zeros. The American pilots unleashed a chatter of .50 caliber fire from six heavy machine guns and they unleashed 37mm shells from their cannon. In seconds, the Americans had blown two Zeros out of the air and they had badly damaged the other two that wobbled precariously and sputtered away.

Other P-38 pilots pounced on more 11 Squadron Zeros with the same vicious strafing and 37mm cannon attacks. The Zeros tried to bank and arch and dive and climb and run. Nakajima's pilots had the knack and speed to maneuver. But the P-38s were too fast. They could always catch up to the Zeros again or outrun them. And the American pilots had disciplined themselves well, making no attempt to engage the Zero pilots in gyrating dogfights. Within five minutes, the surprising P-38s had downed nine Japanese Zeros and damaged several more. Zeros exploded in mid air, burst into flames, lost tails or wings, or props. They cartwheeled, tumbled, or spun dizzily into the Solomon Sea.

Experienced pilots like Saburo Sakai and the sober faced Hiroyashi Nishizawa had suddenly found themselves faced with a fighter plane that was obviously superior to their Zero. Only through their long years of experience and instinct in the air did they avoid death. In fact, Private Nishizawa shot one of the P-38s out of the air when he made an unusually sharp turn and caught the diving pursuer off balance. Before the P-38 pilot could react, Nishizawa had been on top of him, sending 20mm shells into the Lightning. The P-38 exploded and tumbled to earth.

Still, the kill had been a small consolation. Among those who lost their lives before this new, devastating fighter plane was the 11 Squadron commander himself, Lt. Cmdr. Tadashi Nakajima. The squadron leader had caught two 37mm hits in the fuselage and the aircraft had simply exploded in mid air, tearing apart the 11th commander and his plane.

Pilots of surviving Zeros, now without their leader, and fully aware of their peril, sped their planes in a half dozen directions to escape these horrifying, twin engine monsters.

The formation of American bombers, without interruption, now droned over Gasmata. Col. Dwight Devine's B-26s, from 5,000 feet, unleashed four thousand pounders from each aircraft that struck squarely on the Gasmata runways, digging huge craters that would take one to two weeks to repair. Then came more B-26s of the 22nd Bomb Group, dropping more thousand pounders on the same runway, along with taxiways, revetment areas, and parked aircraft. The Marauders left burned Betty bombers and destroyed buildings along with a wrecked runway. One bomb struck an ammunition dump that exploded so violently the ground shuddered as though struck by a .7 Richter scale earthquake.

With no more Zeros to fight, the P-38s came down to rake Gasmata Drome with heavy strafing fire and 37mm shells to ignite more fires, to destroy more aircraft on the ground, and to burn supply dumps. At 1415 hours, when the last

American plane left the area and droned south-ward over the Solomon Sea, Gasmata lay in the same shambles as the other Japanese bases.

When the B-26s and P-38s were gone, Lt. Toshio Handa came out of his shelter under the trees and stared at the devastation on the airfield. Fires blazed everywhere as burning planes belched more flame from secondary explosions. So far as he could see, not a single G-M 4 bomber had escaped destruction or damage. What the B-26s had missed, the P-38s had finished off with their strafing guns and 37mm cannon.

An aide now came next to Lieutenant Handa. "Honorable Commander," he bowed before the officer, "I must report other unfortunate tidings."

Handa merely looked at the man.

"The courageous, dedicated Commander Nakajima was killed in combat with these new American fighter planes."

Handa merely squeezed his face.

"Since our runway is no longer in condition to take aircraft, I have taken some liberties," the aide continued. "I have radioed the 11 Squadron pilots to return to Rabaul or Arawe since there is no way they can land here. It is my understanding that P/lc Saburo Sakai has followed these instructions."

"And were their losses as bad as ours?" Handa finally spoke.

"They have lost at least a dozen Mitsubishi fighter planes, Honorable Handa. Further, some of the other fighter pilots have run off and now wander over the Solomon Sea or along the New Britain coast. Perhaps some may safely reach Arawe."

Lieutenant Handa merely nodded.

"What is your pleasure, Lieutenant?"

The 35 Squadron leader looked at the holocaust on the airfield and then shook his head. "There will be no pleasure. There is nothing we can do now. It is obvious that the Yankee dogs have brought fatal tragedy to us. Not I, not Captain Shingo in Buna, and not Captain Saito in Lae can do a thing. We find ourselves in a most helpless condition."

"But there is still Rabaul and Arawe."

But Handa only shook his head again. "I fear this day will mark a tragic day for us in this struggle. I have merely lost aircraft as have our other air leaders, but my heart aches for General Horii and his troops in New Guinea, far from Buna and deep on the other side of the Owen Stanley Mountains. What is to become of him if he can no longer get air support?"

The aide did not answer.

"Assemble repair crews," Handa gestured. "See what can be done."

"Yes, Honorable Handa."

On the homeward flight of the Americans, the crews of the B-26s stared in awe at the crazy shaped P-38s about them. These bomber crews recognized a sober truth: the Allies now had a fighter plane that could deal with the Zero. Col. Dwight Devine himself stared intently at the strange, boxlike Lightning beyond his cabin window and he could almost visualize the grins on the faces of the fighter pilots. Then Devine turned to his co-pilot.

"Lieutenant, did you ever see anything like that? Fighter planes that could drive Zeros from the sky?"

"No sir, Colonel," Lt. Walter Kell shook his head. "I don't care what the goddamn things look like. I know one thing: if we go out again and those silly looking things are at our side, I'll feel pretty comfortable." Kell nodded, more to himself than to the 22nd Group commander. "After what happened back there at Gasmata, I got a feeling this war has been turned around. We hit hard today, and if those other units with their parafrag bombs were as good as this P-38, those Nips will soon be on the losing end of this goddamn war."

"Whitehead planned well," Devine said. "I'd guess the other air units did do well. The Japanese won't be able to mount a plane anywhere south of Rabaul or east of Madang after today — if we keep up the pressure."

"Yeh," Kell nodded.

By 1630 hours, after the last B-26 touched down at Moresby, elation reigned throughout the Allied base. The air strikes on this 22 September afternoon had come off perfectly, especially with the parafrag bomb. 5th Air Force had knocked out air power in Papua and Gasmata—at least for a while. They had also hurt the Nankai Shitai Force at Ioribaiwa, for Major Welch and his 35th Squadron P-39s had hit the forward Japanese base four times

272

during the course of the afternoon. Horii's positions were now a mass of flame and smoke and he would need to be totally resupplied before he continued the drive to Moresby.

Gen. Basil Morris, at his headquarters in Moresby held a dinner to honor Bent Nose Whitehead for his stunning aerial victory today. "General, you and your air lads did a hell of a job today; finished off those Nips for sure."

However, Ennis Whitehead did not share Morris's total confidence. "I'll drink a toast with you, Basil, but these air attacks today are not the end. We still have two important tasks for 5th Air Force. First, we've got to make certain we keep those Japanese air fields out of commission so they can't send out planes to repay us in kind. Secondly, we now have the job of driving the Japanese ground forces out of Papua."

"We're on our way for that," Morris said. "We're getting more combat troops into this thing. If your airmen keep up the pressure, my ground troops will drive the bloody Nips back."

Morris, of course, did have a point. There would soon be more than 10,000 Allied combat troops in New Guinea to assault General Horii's tired and battered Nankai Shitai Detachment at Ioribaiwa. If 5th Air Force could now erode the long Japanese supply line from Buna, the Nankai would die in the Owen Stanley Mountains. Further, Kenney and MacArthur had authorized an airlift of more American combat troops from the 32nd Infantry Division. With Gasmata knocked out, the Allies could now move troops up the coast from Milne Bay, at the eastern end of New Guinea, to establish a base at Pongani, 50 miles south of Buna. With troops at Pongani, the Allies could begin a pincer movement that would cut off and totally destroy Horii's troops in the Owen Stanleys.

Despite Whitehead's caution, excitement radiated from the Allied airbases around Port Moresby. At 7 Mile Drome, the crews of the B-17 and B-26 units had assembled in their grass shack day rooms to recount their outstanding success this afternoon with their heavy aircraft. They talked of their low level bomb runs and the huge craters they had left in Japanese airstrips. They spoke of the utter surprise they had caused at Lae and Buna, and B-26 crews spoke of the awesome job the P-38s had done on the Japanese Zeros.

"I don't think we'll have to go back too soon," Col. Dick Carmichael said. "And old man Whitehead was something—excited as a kid. He couldn't get over the job we did on Lae."

"Well I can tell you, those P-38s are something," Colonel Devine said. "I couldn't believe their speed and climb and firepower. Those Lightnings are going to make a difference in this war, I can tell you."

At 7 Mile Drome, A/C Frank Lukis, Lt. Larry Jackson and other pilots and crews of the 9th RAAF Group felt the same elation. They had practically wiped out the Salamaua airbase and nearly two full squadrons of Zeros on the ground.

"We showed those Yanks, we did," Jackson

274

grinned. "We're as good as they are. There wasn't one thing still intact by the time we left Sala-maua; not a thing."

"We did a good job," Commander Lukis nodded, "but we can't get overconfident. You never know about those sneaky Nips. Everytime we get the blighters down, they seem to bounce back. Whitehead needs to keep up the pressure; can't give the Nips any rest. That's where the Nips made their mistake. They knocked out our run-ways last month, but they didn't keep up the pres-sure. If they did, they might still 'ave us grounded."

"What do you think we'll do next?" somebody asked.

"Concentrate on Ioribaiwa and the Nip supply line, I'd guess," Lukis said. "I 'eard the Yank lads from 8 Group 'ave all but wiped out the Nips at Ioribaiwa with a 'alf dozen parachute bomb strikes this afternoon. I 'ope so; it'll make it easier for our Diggers up there on Imita Ridge."

At 12 Mile Drome, the P-39 pilots of the 8th and 35th Group listened in awe to the P-38 pilots, those who had met the Zero fighter pilots on al-most even terms over Gasmata. They heard men like Tom Lynch and Bob Faurot recount their climb to 40,000 feet before they simply dove down on the unsuspecting Japanese pilots to massacre them. The Lightnings had outrun, out-dove, and outclimbed the Zeros.

"It's like I told you earlier, Colonel," Tom Lynch said to Boyd Wagner, "They're gonna switch all our fighter groups over to P-38s. After our performance today, they have to. The P-38 is going to change this New Guinea war."

"Maybe," a fighter plane pilot said, "but you should have seen those B-25s over Buna; the most amazing thing I ever saw: ten big strafing guns like an artillery barrage, and emptying those parafrags by the hundreds. Those converted Mitchells did more damage with 16 planes than conventional bombers could have done with a hundred planes. Maybe the P-38 will be our fighter plane of the future, but B-25s like those today over Buna will be doing all the work in the future."

"I guess that Pappy Gunn is something at that," another 8th Group pilot said.

And, at 3 Mile Drome, in the grass shack day room, came perhaps the most greatest excitement of all. The 3rd Bomb Group with their A-20s and then the awesome converted B-25s had caused the most damage of all on this 22 September day. They had reaffirmed their title as "Most hated by Japanese air commanders." It had been the third that initiated the parafrag in combat over Iori-baiwa, the 3rd's A-20s that had pulverized Lae today, and the 3rd's B-25s that had caused astonishing destruction to a hundred aircraft at Buna. While the 3rd Group air men congratulated themselves on this fact, Major Strickland suddenly sobered in a reflective mood. He turned seriously to the others.

"We owe Pappy Gunn plenty," the major said. "He's the man who converted our A-20s and B-25s. It's like Colonel Davies says—these low level

A-20s and B-25s will change the air war in New Guinea."

"Yeh," Captain Hall nodded. "We owe the Mad Professor a lot." He looked at big John Davies. "What do you say, Colonel?"

"I can't disagree with you, Don," the 3rd Group commander said. "But now that we've got the initiative, we can't let go. I think we'll be going back to Lae and Buna and Salamaua, and even Gasmata; we'll be going back every day if we can to keep those fields out of commission. They'll hit the Nip supply lines and make their ground troops rot in the jungles of the Owen Stanleys."

"Jesus, Colonel," an airman grinned, "don't you think we deserve a few days rest after today? We earned it."

"No chance," Davies shook his head. "You never know about those Japanese. We hit them hard today, sure, but that doesn't mean they'll quit. If we relax or get complacent, those Nips will be right on top of us again."

Big John Davies was certainly correct for the Japanese had reacted quickly after the multiple air strikes on their four major air bases that supported the Papuan campaign. At 1800 hours, 22 September 1942, Gen. Tomitaro Horii called Capt. Masahisa Saito in Lae.

"Captain, you cannot understand the punishment we have taken today from the enemy devil tactics. Our positions are in shambles. Our supplies are gone and unless we get relief quickly, we will be forced to withdraw from Ioribaiwa. We have not lost many troops from the parachute bomb attacks, but our supplies are gone and no army can survive without food, medicine, and ammunition. We have suffered untold agony and discomfort in this drive across the the Owen Stanley Mountains. You must stop these enemy air assaults and you must protect our supply lines. We would suffer a tragedy indeed if we were forced to give up our gains."

"I understand our distress," Captain Saito said, "but surely, you know the tragedy that befell our airbases this afternoon. We cannot mount aircraft, even if we had any aircraft left to fly."

"Captain," Horii said soberly, "tragedies are a fact of life in war. Every Samurai accepts defeat, but the true Samurai always rebounds to fight again. We have suffered our own defeats, but we will willingly fight on. We will die for the Emperor if necessary. Surely, one attack on your airdromes, no matter how seriously, cannot mean the end. You too must rebound in the tradition of the good Samurai."

"You are correct, Honorable Horii," Captain Saito said. "I feel ashamed with this defeatist attitude. In truth, I have been thinking of alternatives ever since these enemy air attacks this afternoon. I will act at once to overcome these misfortunes we have all suffered today. I will find means to extract vengeance from our enemies."

"Thank you, Captain," General Horii said. "Your promise renews our hopes here in Ioribaiwa. I leave once more our fortunes in your hands."

"By the will of our spirit ancestors, I shall not fail you," Captain Masahisa Saito told the Nankai Shitai Detachment commander.

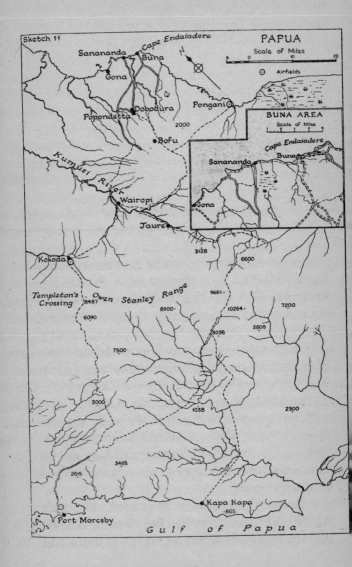

Sketch 11

PAPUA

Scale of Miles

5   0   5   10   20

⊙   Airfields

Cape Endaiadere

Sanananda   Buna

Gona

Dobodura   Pongani ◯

Popondetta   2000

Bofu

Kumusi River

Wairopi

Jaure

BUNA AREA

Scale of Miles

Cape Endaiadere

Sanananda   Buna

Gona

Kokoda ◯   3128   6600

Templeton's   Owen Stanley Range   9661
Crossing   8487

6090   8900   10264   7200

3036   2808

7500

3000   2300

1038

3465

2615   Kapa Kapa
       ·665

Port Moresby

Gulf   of   Papua

CHAPTER SIXTEEN

On the early evening of 22 September 1942, Capt. Masahisa Saito reached Adm. Junichi Kasaka. The 24th Air Flotilla commander had already guessed the nature of the call from his Tinian Wing commander and he listened soberly.

"General Horii expects us to recover from these afternoon air tragedies," Saito said, "and I agree with the honorable Nankai Shitai commander."

"But you have no airbases," Kasaka said.

"I can promise that within the week the airfields in Papua will be repaired," Saito answered. "We will again be able to base aircraft here and we can again cover the skies of the Owen Stanleys with such aircraft."

Admiral Kasaka was unimpressed. The 24th Air Flotilla commander had been feeding aircraft into the Solomons where the fight was touch and go in this late September. Further, he doubted that Saito or Shingo could repair the bases in Papua within a week, especially if Allied air units struck the bases again. Also, Kasaka was appalled at the high loss of grounded planes during the 5th Air Force multiple raids and he was not sure he could replace even half of these planes. Captain Saito had been forced to send one squadron of his Tinian Wing and the fragments of another squadron up to Madang, while the remnants of 11 Squadron had been forced to fly to Arawe. Kasaka's nearest bases to Moresby now were Rabaul, Arawe, and Madang, and the admiral was reluctant to replace the dozens of Zeros, Vals, and Bettys at bases so distant from Moresby.

Nonetheless, Kasaka listened to Saito. "We have already begun the repairs on the Lae runways," the Tinian Wing commander said, "and we will have the airstrips ready soon. I promise, never again will the Tinian Wing be caught off guard. Our squadrons will remain ever vigilant to stop further attempts to attack Lae."

"We cannot be certain of that, Captain," Kasaka said.

"Our pilots of the Tinian Wing are eager to fly again, eager to avenge our losses," Saito insisted. "There is still time to win Port Moresby, if we maintain our resolve."

"But you will need to fly from Arawe and Madang at the moment, and these bases are many miles from Port Moresby."

"Our pilots are willing," Saito persisted. "We

will gladly fly these long distances until we repair our airfields."

Admiral Kasaka gave in. "I will speak to General Imamura, but I can give you but a hundred aircraft if the Honorable Imamura agrees. I will send Emily flying boats to Lae and Salamaua harbors to pick up your pilots and return them to Rabaul. They can fly the new aircraft to Madang and protect Lae from there until you repair your airbases."

"Thank you, Admiral," Captain Saito said.

Admiral Kasaka reported to General Imamura and explained the urgent request from Captain Saito. "Horii badly needs air support if he is to continue his drive to Port Moresby. I hope you will not think me brash to promise Captain Saito a hundred aircraft, despite our struggle in the Solomons."

"I would agree," Imamura said, surprising the 24th Flotilla commander. "After all, we cannot ignore the reconnaisance reports. The enemy is flying combat troops over the mountains to Cape Nelson on the north coast of Papua, and fifty miles east of Buna. They are also moving troops to Cape Nelson from their base at Milne Bay."

"I am familiar with this reconnaissance report," Kasaka said.

"We can assume the enemy intends to entrap the Nankai Shitai Force in the Owen Stanley Mountains," General Imamura said. "Should the Allies succeed, we would suffer tragedy indeed." He looked at a map on his desk. "They obviously plan to occupy the Cape Nelson peninsula and then march overland to the Buna-Gona area. I would ask that you indeed send these aircraft to Madang and Arawe and to repair your airfields at Lae and Buna with all haste."

"I will do so."

"I intend to send to the Buna-Gona area some elements of the Kawaguchi Detachment that unfortunately failed in its mission to Milne Bay. We can also send along the 5th Sasebo Landing Force and the 67th Field Hospital. Finally, we can send the 14th and 15th Construction Battalion who can aid in the repair of the Buna airstrips and who can also build strong defense bunkers in the Buna-Gona area." He paused. "I would ask, Admiral Kasaka, that your air units furnish protection when these reinforcements sail for Buna."

"Of course," Kusaka said. "We will bring more planes into Arawe and we shall work feverishly to repair the fields at Gasmata and Lae."

"Good," Gen. Hitoshi Imamura nodded. He referred to his map again. "The Pioneer Battalion will construct a series of interlocking bunkers along the Sanandana Track and the Cape Endaiadere Track. The bunkers will be so constructed as to allow the shifting of forces under strong protection if needed. These same defenses will allow General Horii to escape safely to the Buna area from the Owen Stanley positions should such a retirement become necessary. The Honorable Horii will be able to withdraw from the westward, away from a possible enemy ground thrust from the Cape Nelson area."

Now Admiral Kasaka pointed to the map. "We

shall conduct air sorties from our improved base at Arawe to attack these vessels and barges from Milne Bay, and we will attack this new enemy airfield under construction at Cape Nelson to thwart further movement of Allied ground troops over the mountains. Such assaults will serve a double purpose. The air attacks will hamper the enemy movements to Cape Nelson and the attacks will serve as a diversion while the Kawaguchi Detachment sails to Buna."

"Excellent," General Imamura said. "We will begin at once."

On the very evening of 22 September three transport vessels under escort of three destroyers and the cruisers *Tenryu* and *Tatsuta* left Rabaul and headed for Buna. By morning the vessels were expected to clear Dampier Strait on the western tip of New Britain to begin the sail over the Solomon Sea to Buna. On the same evening, Emily flying boats landed at both the Lae and Salamaua harbors to pick up fighters pilots from the Tinian Wing and take them back to Rabaul. The pilots would fly back the next day with new Zeros to Madang and to operate from there until the Lae base was repaired. Meanwhile, Kasaka sent a squadron of Betty bombers and a squadron of Zeros to Arawe where they would operate until the Gasmata base was repaired.

However, these renewed strategies by the Japanese commanders would be a case of too little too late. The 22 September air strikes had drastically changed the fortunes of the New Guinea campaign. The raids had heightened the morale of

Allied airmen and ground troops, while the air strikes had demoralized the Japanese. When the Tinian Wing pilots flew to Rabaul to pick up new Zeros, they did so with little enthusiasm, for they remembered too vividly the dreadful parafrag bomb attacks and they had listened in awe to reports of this new American P-38 fighter plane that had killed the renowned 11 Squadron of Lt. Cmdr. Tadashi Nakajima. Further, if these pilots flew to Madang instead of to Lae, they could not help feeling they were in retreat.

At Ioribaiwa, the common Nankai Shitai soldier felt panic after the unopposed parafrag bomb attacks on 22 September. No matter how much their officers encouraged them, or how enthusiastically General Horii or Colonel Yokoyama spoke to them, the soldiers responded with quiet reserve, not the shouting, confident "Banzai!" that had been their war cry for nearly ten months.

And in truth, the first evidence in these changes of fortune came when the 3rd and 38th Bomb Groups with P-38 escorts came over the Solomon Sea at mid-morning of 23 September to attack the five ship convoy carrying reinforcements of men and supplies to Buna. While the 3rd and 38th did not sink any ships, the low level parafrag attacks by A-20s and B-25s had set afire the ships from one end to the other. The heavy strafing fire from nose guns had raked the decks so badly, that hundreds of Japanese on board had suffered death or injury.

The Japanese could only mount a dozen Zeros

from Arawe to intercept the American bombers. Maj. Tom Lynch and Capt. Bob Faurot with the P-38 pilots gave these Zero pilots the same lesson the P-38 pilots had given 11 Squadron pilots over Gasmata. Within moments, Lynch and his pilots shot down six of the Zeros and sent the rest scurrying in retreat.

Horii would get no reinforcements, for the battered Japanese convoy fled the Solomon Sea and hurried back to Rabaul.

When the debacle had ended, Davies cried into his radio. "Okay, boys, let's go home."

Australian reinforcement troops at Imita Ridge, meanwhile, had begun to pound the Japanese troops at Ioribaiwa with 75 pounder artillery shells, while American and Australian planes battered the Nankai Shitai positions with parafrag bombs. By the evening of 27 September, a fresh Australian brigade joined the one that arrived at Imita Ridge on 22 September. As soon as the Japanese positions at Ioribaiwa had been softened enough, the nearly 5,000 fresh Australian troops would move into Ioribaiwa against the Japanese to drive them out.

The Japanese held on tenaciously at Ioribaiwa despite the artillery pounding and the constant parafrag strikes. Horii still maintained an air of optimism, expecting any day to see new supplies come from the Kokoda Trail and to see new formations of Zeros again droning over Ioribaiwa.

Gen. Ennis Bent Nose Whitehead refused to give the Japanese a single day of respite following the 22 September raids. Almost daily, he sent out bombers and fighter bombers to attack the Iori-baiwa positions, the Japanese supply lines from Buna, and the airstrips at Buna, Salamaua, Lae and Gasmata.

Whenever weather permitted, A-20s, P-39s, P-40s, and even the new P-38s, using all purpose as well as parafrag bombs, hit the Japanese in the Owen Stanleys. The aerial assaults chewed up troop concentrations and set fire to supplies. Further, the B-25s, B-26s, and B-17s under fighter escort continually pounded the airstrips, leaving the Japanese caught in a vicious cycle that Whitehead had hoped for. Even on the few days that Allied planes had not hit these bases, the Japanese could not repair their airstrips before the medium and heavy bombers were back again, destroying whatever progress the Japanese had made on runways. Thus, both the Tinian and 4th Kokutai Wings had no runways to base planes that could fight back against the Allied air assaults.

The Allies could now make strikes on the airbases with impunity because of the lack of Zero interceptors. Both Captain Saito and Captain Shingo suffered in agonizing helplessness as they saw Allied bombers and fighters come over their airfields day after day to undo whatever repair work they had begun.

At Ioribaiwa, on 27 September, with two infantry brigades ready to move against the Japanese, General Horii called his staff. He tightened his face to restrain tears. "More than a month has passed since the Shitai departed Rabaul to follow the gallant Yokoyama advance butai," Horii began. "We have crushed strong positions at Isurava, Iora, Kokoda, the Gap, and Efogi. We have advanced swiftly after fierce battle and we destroyed the final enemy resistance at Ioribaiwa." He paused and sighed. "Each tai has marched over the mountains and through deep valleys, conquered great heights, and pursued the Australians for more than twenty days. We have waded through deep rivers, scaled breathtaking cliffs, uncomplainingly carried heavy burdens over the reportedly impregnable Owen Stanley Range. The reason we halted was to regain our fighting strength before striking a decisive blow at Moresby."

Horii paused again, this time wiping a tear from his eye. "But now, we have suffered an unexpected change of fortunes at this moment of victory. Our troops have empty stomachs and the devil tactics of the Allied air forces has left grave imperfections in our supply line. They have destroyed our airfields and we no longer have air support. With regret I must tell you the battle is lost. Our scouts report the arrival of fresh Australian troops, and they now prepare to overrun our positions. I know that many of you would stay here and fight to the death, but it would only be a futile effort. We have no choice but to retire as swiftly and orderly as possible."

A company commander, a mere captain, bravely stepped forward in the midst of the high brass circled around General Horii. "Honorable Horii, it is a sorry thing to leave behind the bodies of our comrades on the ground we have so dearly won. Please, let us fight to the end."

"You are brave as well as bold to interrupt this conference," Horii said. "No, Captain, we will not stay. Our troops have suffered enough." He turned to one of his battalion commanders, Lt. Col. Ita Horie. "I would ask, Colonel, that your battalion assume the important responsibility of rear guard while we retire to Kokoda. But," he gestured emphatically, "you will abandon your positions at the first opportunity."

"We will not fail, Honorable Horii," Lieutenant Colonel Horie said.

Now Col. Yosuke Yokoyama, who also disagreed with Horii's decision to retreat, made a plea himself. "Honorable Horii, we are told that our Mitsubishi fighter planes will again cover the skies over the Owen Stanley Mountains as soon as they repair the airdrome at Lae. Captain Saito has promised this and he is an honorable officer. For every hour we delay the Australians, we give our reinforcements at Buna another hour to strengthen their defenses."

"We must face the truth, Yosuke," Horii said, "the reinforcements did not reach Buna. Our supply lines are in ruins. We must retreat. Despite Captain Saito's promises, he cannot help us. The Allied air forces strike Ioribaiwa with impunity as they strike our air bases and our supply lines."

True, the 5th Air Force continued to thwart any possibility of new air support for the Japanese. The 43rd, 90th, and 22nd continued to plaster Gasmata and now Arawe. The heavies also struck shipping and dock facilities at Rabaul to forestall any reinforcements to Buna. The 3rd and the newly arrived 38th Bomb Group continually hit Lae, Salamaua, and Buna, further eliminating the possibility of basing planes here again. Other air units pounded Japanese supply lines, ending hopes for resupply to the Nankai Shitai force in the Owen Stanleys.

General Horii began his retreat over the Owen Stanleys by the 1st of October, trying to hold at Deniki, at Templeton's Crossing, at Kokoda, or at Oivi. The Australians continued their hot pursuit and the Allied air units continually harassed the retreating Japanese, while not a single Japanese plane rose in defense of the Japanese ground forces. The Nankai Shitai offensive in Papua had totally collapsed.

Horii, a rare Samurai officer who felt sympathy for his men, cried openly when he learned that the Horie battalion had been annihilated. They had made the ultimate sacrifice on his behalf. Horii also mourned the continued loss of men from hunger and disease. Many Japanese soldiers were on the verge of death, gaunt and dehydrated from lack of medicine and food. Others suffered from tropical sores and ulcers on their faces, limbs, and torsos; or they were weak from dengue and malarial fever. Their uniforms were in tatters, mere rags, and they had no means to replace them.

Such was the state of the Japanese ground soldier after the 5th Air Force took utter control of the New Guinea skies.

All along the route, Horii left behind the dead to rot in the jungle. He could only offer those left behind the warrior prayer of the Samurai, with the closing lines: "Sleep peacefully, my friend; farewell, we shall meet again in Heaven."

Finally, the straggling horde of troops, 4,000 men, less than half of those who had come up from Buna, reached the Kumusi River. This was the last obstacle before the safety of the Buna defenses. But here, where the thousands of troops waited with eagerness to escape the pursuing Australians, Horii would suffer the worst defeat of the Papuan campaign.

On 10 November, with thousands of Australian infantry troops only hours from the Kumusi River, the several thousand Japanese troops of the Nankai Shitai Force was ready to cross the Kumusi. They found the river swollen from recent rains and rushing like escaping waters from a collapsed dam. Water had risen close to the log planking of the wire rope suspension bridge. However, Japanese engineers said the bridge was safe to cross.

"We will cross in double file," Horii told his subordinates. "Once we have reached the other side, we will destroy this bridge to stop the hot pursuit of the Australians. Our troops will discard all but their rifles, pistols, and swords." He looked at Colonel Yokoyama. "Your men will cross first since they have suffered the worst."

"And what of yourself, Honorable Horii? You should go first, for your leadership will be sorely needed at Buna."

"Colonel," Horii barked, "I gave an order."

"Yes, General," Colonel Yosuke Yokoyama nodded.

General Horii stood on the south bank and directed his Japanese soldiers to the bridge. "Hurry! Find strength within yourselves to move swiftly."

The soldiers responded, hobbling, limping, skipping. The more able helped the less able. The troops were moving quickly and orderly when Horii heard the distant boom Australian cannon in the dense jungles behind him. Still, he hoped to cross the Kumusi before any Diggers arrived. Horii then suddenly heard the drone of planes.

Col. John Davies was leading all four squadrons of his 3rd Bomb Group, 24 B-25s and 24 A-20s. When he looked down at the swollen Kumusi, he gaped in astonishment. He could not believe the sight: troops jammed on the wobbly wire rope bridge, hordes of other troops on the south bank waiting to cross. In all his months of war, Davies had never seen a more helpless, fat target. He almost hesitated for he would indeed be shooting proverbial fish in a barrel. But reality struck Davies. These were the enemy and every one who survived would be a potential killer of an American or Australian soldier who advanced on Buna. And Davies, like everyone else, knew there *would* be a battle at Buna.

Big John Davies picked up his radio. "We'll start with the bridge. Our lead Vs will go in first with fragmentation bombs and the 90th Squadron will follow with incendiary parafrags."

"Yes sir," Capt. Jim Hennebry answered.

Then began the aerial massacre of Nankai Shitai on the Kumusi River.

First came B-25s, shooting deadly streams of .50 caliber fire from ten nose guns on each plane. The withering fire killed or maimed dozens of Japanese troops, many of whom fell and tumbled into the swollen Kumusi to drown if they were not already dead. Then came the drifting parafrags, hitting the bridge and blowing away hordes of men with exploding shrapnel. Next came the deadly incendiaries of the 90th and 89th Squadrons. Jim Hennebry tightened his face, looking in horror as the parachute incendiaries struck the span accurately at low level to explode and ignite smoke and fire.

Log flooring and human beings caught fire, emitting a pungent odor of burning hardwood mixed with burning flesh. By the time the last A-20 had dropped its incendiary bombs on the helpless victims, the burning bridge snapped and plopped into the rushing Kumusi River, dumping countless Japanese soldiers into the torrent.

General Horii was utterly stunned, almost in a catatonic state. Two young officers dragged the Nankai Shitai commander into some sheltering trees, away from the heavy strafing fire.

After the 3rd Bomb Group aircraft were gone, Horii came out his numbed state and quickly ordered his men to lash together log rafts to cross the swift moving river. They must get across or the oncoming Australians might annihilate whatever was left of his soldiers.

"Hurry! Hurry!" Horii cried. "At once!"

Soon, dozens of hastily constructed rafts plopped into the water and men clambered aboard, using tree limbs as oars to reach the other side. Horii had climbed on one of the rafts with three soldiers to make the perilous crossing against the boiling torrent. Suddenly, a glob of water caught Horii's improvised raft on one side and flipped it over, dumping Horii and his soldiers into the swollen, rushing stream. From another raft, Col. Yosuke Yokoyama stared in horror. He saw the general's head bob only once before Horii disappeared under the swirling water.

"Farewell, brave Samurai, until we meet again in heaven," Colonel Yokoyama whispered softly, soberly.

By dark of 11 November, Col. Yosuke Yokoyama, his staff aide, and other officers finally straggled into the outer defense perimeter of the Buna-Gona area with less than 3,000 men, all that remained of the Nankai Shitai Force. Japanese war correspondent Seizo Okada perhaps described best the condition of these survivors:

"Their uniforms were soiled with blood and mud and sweat, torn to pieces. They were infantrymen without rifles, men walking on bare feet, men wearing blankets of straw rice bags instead of uniforms; men reduced to skin and bones plodding along with the help of sticks, men gasping and crawling on the ground; some of them lying there for a while and struggling to their feet again, while others stirred no more."

The Japanese held Samurai rites that night for Gen. Tomitaro Horii, Maj. Tadashi Horie, Capt. Masuma Takase, Capt. Kenyo Sakamoto, and the thousands of other courageous Japanese warriors who had perished in the Owen Stanley fight during the past three months or more. Then the Japanese dug in at Buna to await the Allied onslaught that was sure to come.

5th Air Force planes soon enough swarmed over the Buna area and the Solomon Sea like unchecked locusts, for the 24th Air Flotilla had expended itself, both in the Solomons and in New Guinea. On the ground, 15,000 heavily armed American and Australian troops, supplied with every manner of weapon, including tanks, launched their first attack against Buna on 16 November. They made little progress on this first day. However, from a practical standpoint, a Japanese defeat at Buna was inevitable. The Allies had overwhelming air and ground superiority.

Gen. Hitoshi Imamura faced a dilemma. The 8th Area Forces commander no longer had the means to support both the Solomons and New Guinea fights. He concluded that while he might still win in Guadalcanal, the cause at Buna was hopeless. So he wrote off Buna, leaving to commanders the decision to fight on or to retire through the jungles to Salamaua and Lae or across the Solomon Sea to New Britain.

The 9,000 troops at Buna-Gona elected to fight. The two month Buna campaign became one of the most vicious and exhausting battles in military history. The story of the Buna battle has been told many times and only a recap is necessary.

The Japanese simply resisted tenaciously, with determination and courage, knowing they would die from hunger, disease, or the Allied enemy. Still, they fought the hopeless battle, forcing the Americans and Australians to pry them from one bunker after another. The Japanese had even stacked their dead before them as improvised sandbags to further deter Digger and GI assaults. Not until 23 January 1943 did the GIs of the 32nd Infantry Division slay the last Japanese survivor on the beaches of Buna. The Buna-Gona fight had been so exhausting, that the Aussies and Americans would need months of recuperation before they could go into battle again.

Gen. Douglas MacArthur had finally concluded Operation Providence, the initial step in Task Two—the reconquest of Papuan New Guinea. The effort, however, had been a six month nightmare in the toughest fighting in the world. The campaign in this hostile terrain had cost the Japanese 13,000 lives. The Americans lost 2,800 men and the Australians had lost 5,700 men. More than half of these deaths from hunger and disease.

Heroes abounded on both sides. Among the famed Japanese Tinian Wing, almost every Japanese pilot except P/lc Saburo Sakai and Capt. Masahisa Saito died in combat during the Papuan campaign or in subsequent campaigns. In the 4th Kokutai Wing, both Capt. Uehara Shingo and Cmdr. Bunji Shimada survived the war, but

Lt. Toshio Handa died in a bombing raid over the Solomons. In the Nankai Shitai Force, all but Col. Yosuke Yokoyama among the ground troop commanders were killed during the Buna campaign.

Among the Americans, Maj. Bob Strickland survived the war, but Col. John Davies returned to the United States in 1943 and returned to the Pacific later to lead a B-29 Wing. Col. Boyd "Buzz" Wagner also returned to the United States in 1943. He was killed in a P-40 crash at Elgin Air Force base only a month after his return from New Guinea. Capt. Tom Lynch, who led the first P-38 formations in combat, died in his P-38 when the plane was hit by ack ack fire during an attack on the Admiralties in March of 1943.

Paul "Pappy" Gunn survived the war and returned to the Philippines to again operate a commercial airline. On 11 October 1947, while flying a plane load of lumber from Manila to Lingayen Gulf, his aircraft got caught in a sudden wind storm and crashed. He died instantly.

Among the Australians, Lt. Larry Jackson survived the war despite a hard campaign and returned to business in Melbourne. Both A/C Frank Lukis and Gen. Basil Morris, who also survived the war, remained in the military until retirement.

Military historians will long debate the Papuan fight. How did the campaign turn from an expected Allied defeat to a total Japanese wipe out? The tactics of Allied air and ground commanders on both sides were quite sound and no one could dispute the courage of ground troops and airmen from both sides. There seems no doubt that the issue was turned around during the September crises.

If any man or incident brought a turning point, perhaps the man was Paul Pappy Gunn and the incident was the coordinated 5th Air Force attacks in 22 September 1942. Gunn had adopted the parafrag bomb, modified the B-25 and A-20 as a low level attack bomber, and altered the C-47 Gooney Bird to carry heavy equipment. All of these innovations badly hurt the Japanese. The 22 September raids, featuring the modified B-25s and the parafrag, began the deterioration of the 24th Japanese Air Flotilla in the Papuan campaign. Like a baseball team that fails without good pitching, the Nankai Shitai Force failed without air support.

In a tribute to Paul Gunn, Australian war correspondent Pat Robinson, who traveled with the Australian Diggers throughout the Papuan campaign, had this to say: "New air techniques by aircraft gained a new significance in the Papuan campaign, especially when the combat plane was manipulated to meet the conditions present. In the Southwest Pacific, such transport aircraft tactics opened the way to operations hitherto deemed impossible."

Gen. Basil Morris had said after the campaign: "Air power made the difference. I was grateful to have had the support of the greatest and most courageous air fighting forces in the world."

Maj. Mitsuo Koiwa, the survivor of the Horie

Battalion at Ioribaiwa, said after the war: "When the medium Mitchell bomber became a monster attack plane, we knew our days in New Guinea were numbered. The low level attacks from these B-25s, dropping hundreds of the parachute bombs and strafing with ten heavy guns, caused destruction and fear among our troops. This new B-25 tactic caused more demoralization against our troops than anything else."

And finally, perhaps the Johnny-come-lately P-38 Lightning fighter plane played an important role. Former Japanese airman Saburo Sakai told American interpreter Roger Pineau after the war: "On my first confrontation with the P-38, I was astonished to find an American aircraft that could outrun, outclimb, and outdive our Zero, which we thought was the most superior fighter plane in the world. The Lightning's great speed, its sensational high altitude peformance, and especially its ability to dive and climb much faster than the Zero presented insuperable problems for our fliers. The P-38 pilots, flying at great height, chose when and where they wanted to fight with disastrous results for our own men. The P-38 boded ill for the future and destroyed the morale of the Zero fighter pilot."

The success of Operation Providence ended any further Japanese threats to Australia. Further, the victory in the Papuan campaign opened the doors to the success of Task Two and Douglas MacArthur's eventual return to the Philippines.

The Pacific Siege
PARTICIPANTS

Japanese M-1 Operation
8th Area Armed Forces - Gen. Hitoshi Imamura
4th Fleet - Adm. Sabo Inouye
24th Air Flotilla - Adm. Junichi Kasaka
  Tinian Wing - Capt. Masahisa Saito
    10 Squadron-Lt. Junichi Sasai
    11 Squadron - Lt. Comdr. Tadashi Nakajima
  4th Kokutai Wing - Capt. Uehara Shingo
    B Group - Cmdr. Bunji Shimada
    C Group - Lt. Toshio Handa
Nankai Shitai Detachment (South Sea Detachment)
  Gen. Tomitaro Horii
  Yokoyama Force - Col. Yosuke Yokoyama

Allied Operation Providence
Southwest Pacific Forces - Gen. Douglas MacArthur
  New Guinea Force-Operational commander -
    Gen. Basil Morris
  5th Air Force - Gen. George C. Kenney
  5th Air Force ADVON — Operational com-
    mander - Gen. Ennis Whitehead
    3rd Bomb Group - Col. John Davies
    19th Bomb Group - Col. Richard Carmichael
    22nd Bomb Group - Col. Dwight Devine
    43rd Bomb Group - Maj. William Benn
    8th Fighter Group - Col. Boyd Wagner
    35th Fighter Group - Col. Richard Legg

9th RAAF Group - 22 Squadron - A/C Frank Lukis

75 Squadron - Lt. Larry Jackson

808th Aviation Engineers - Col. Louis Sverdrup

4th Air Depot & 3rd Bomb Group - Maj. Paul Gunn

38th Bomb Group

71st Bomb Squadron - Capt. Larry Tanberg

17th Aug 1943 ⬚53⬚ ⬚49⬚ /38 Wewak

18th Aug 1943 ⬚53⬚ /74 " (3/1)

12th Oct 1943 ⬚83⬚⬚126⬚ /125 Rabaul (2/2) ⑥ ⬚15⬚ ⬚21⬚

18th " " ? /? Rabaul ③

23rd " " ⬚45⬚ /47 " (0/2)

24th " " ⬚62⬚ /54 " ⁻⁰

25th " " ⑥①/50 " (1/0)

29th " " ⬚37⬚ /53 " —

2nd Nov " ⬚108⬚ /102 " (9/13) 12/12 14/15

4th Nov " Navy 97/112 " (3/7)

" " " ⬚27⬚ /67 " (-/1)

7th Nov " ⬚24⬚ /64 " (-/5)

11th

13th

26th

302

BIBLIOGRAPHY

Blair, Clay Jr., *Silent Victory,* Vol. 1, Lippincott & Co., Philadelphia, 1975,

Caiden, Martin, *The Ragged, Rugged Warriors,* Bantam Books, New York City, 1966,

Craven, W.F. and Cate, J.L., *The Army Air Forces in World War II,* University of Chicago Press, Chicago, 1950.

Volume I, *Plans and Early Operations*

Volume IV, *The Pacific: Guadalcanal to Saipan*

Freeman, Roger, *B-17 Fortress at War,* Charles Scribner & Son, New York City, 1977.

Hess, William, *Pacific Sweep,* Doubleday & Company, New York City, 1974.

Jablonski, Edward, *Air War,* Volume I, Doubleday & Company, Garden City, 1971.

Jablonski, Edward, *Flying Fortress,* Doubleday & Company, Garden City, 1965.

Johnson, George, *Pacific Partner,* World Book Company, Australia, reprinted by Duell, Sloan & Pearce, New York City, 1944.

Kenney, George C., *The Saga of Pappy Gunn,* Duell, Sloan & Pearce, New York City, 1959.

Lundstrom, John B., *The Pacific Campaign,* Naval Institute Press, Annapolis, Maryland, 1976.

Maurer, Maurer, *Combat Squadrons of The Air Force, World War II,* U.S. Historical Division, Department of the Air Force, Washington, DC, 1969.

Maurer, Maurer, *Air Force Combat Units of World War II,* U.S. Historical Division, Department of the Air Force, Washington, DC, 1960.

Milner, Samuel, *Victory in Papua,* The United States Army in World War II, The War in the Pacific, Government Printing Office, Washington, DC, 1957.

Morrison, Samuel, *History of U.S. Naval Operations in World War II,* Little & Brown, Boston, 1948.

Volume III, *The Rising Sun in the Pacific.*

Volume IV, *Coral Sea, Midway, and Submarine Action.*

Volume VI, *Breaking the Bismarck Barrier,* "Holding Papua".

Paul, Raymond, *Retreat from Kokoda,* Heinemann Publishers, Melbourne, Aus., 1958.

Robinson, Pat, *The Fight For New Guinea,* First Offensive, Random House, New York City, 1943.

Sakai, Saburo, *Samurai,* Bantam Books, New York City, 1978.

Steinberg, Rafael, *Island Fighting,* Time-Life Books, New York City, 1978.

Sunderman, James W. Major, USAF, *World War II in the Air, the Pacific,* Franklin Watts Inc., New York City, 1962.

Toliver, Raymond and Constable, Trevor, *Fighting Aces,* MacMillan & Co., New York City, 1962.

RECORD SOURCES

National Archives, War Records, Washington, DC -
Mr. James Hastings, Administrative Assistant
  USAFIA Directive #174, Providence Airdromes
    Directive #385, G-3 Files, PROVIDENCE, New
      Guinea
  5th Air Force Operational Plans
    Operations Instruction #25, 3 Oct. 1942
    Operations Instruction #2, 26 Oct. 1942
    Operations Instruction #23, 10 Nov. 1942
    Operations Instruction #42, 14 Nov. 1942
    Operations Instruction #44, 15 Nov. 1942
    Operations Instruction #27, 2 Dec. 1942
  Kenney Operational Order #26, to ADVON 5th Air
    Force, 5 Oct. 1942, "Investment of Buna by U.S.
    Regiment moving from Wanigela Mission"
  32nd U.S. Infantry Divisional Reports, file #1990,
    10-2-42 to 1-24-43
    Section 332-26, Medical Narrative History of
      Papuan Campaign 9/10/42 to 3/17/43
    Section 333-26, Report of Activities in Papuan
      Campaign, 10/2/42 to 1/26/43
    Section 332-2, G-2 Report of Activities in Papuan
      Campaign, 10/20/42 to 1/24/43
JAPANESE RECORDS - ATIS reports (Allied inter-
  rogation translation service) Nankai Shitai Operations
    Order #26 - Eastern New Guinea Operations,
      Mar.-Sept. 1942

Order #293 - Invasion of Eastern New Guinea

Order #28 - Nankai Shitai Operations Order

Order #33 - 17th Army Instruction Summary

Order #6 - 6 August 1942 Instructions

Order #24 - Naval Actions, Japanese Invasion of Eastern New Guinea

Order #4 - Diaries of Yazawa Force and Kura 3rd Battalion "The campaign of the Pacific War"

Nankai Shitai Order #1A-102, 24 Aug. 1942 - "Over the Owen Stanley Mountains"

Nankai Shitai Order #102. 29 Aug. 1942 and 30 Aug 1942

Order #120 - Outline of Southeast Area Naval Air Operations, Part 1, Dec. 1941 to Aug. 1942

Outline of Southwest Area Naval Air Operations, Part III, Sept. 1942 to Jan. 1943

USAF Historical Division, Albert Simpson Historical Center, Maxwell Air Force Base, Ala. - Mr. James N. Eastman Jr., Chief, Research Center

Army Air Force Studies #9 - The AAF in Australia to Summer of 1942

Army Air Force Studies #10 - The AAF in SWPA to Jan. of 1943

Histories:

3rd Bomb Group, Microfilm Reel #B0043

35th Fighter Group, Microfilm Reel #B0116

22nd Bomb Group, Microfilm Reel #A7384

5th Air Force, Microfilm Reel #A7384

5th Air Force, Microfilm Reel #A7385

Australian War Memorial, Canberra City, A.C.T. - Mr. N.J. Flanagan, Director

Pacific Victory, Hugh Buggy, asst. historian

Royal Australian Air Force, 1939-1942, Series 2, Douglas Gillison

Southwest Pacific Area, First Year, Kokada to Wau, Series 1, Dudley McCarthy

The Japanese Thrust, Series 3, Lionel Wigmore

OTHER SOURCES

Combat History of the 32nd Infantry Division, prepared by Public Relations Director, office of 32nd Division

History of the 3rd Bomb Group, prepared by Public Relations of 3rd Bomb Group

History of the 38th Bomb Group, prepared by Mr. John Henry, military affairs historian

Narrative of Sergeant F.K. Darrow, 822nd Squadron, 38th Bomb Group

Narrative of Colonel F.G. Hoffman, Retired, 81st Depot Repair Squadron, 4th Air Depot, who aided Major Gunn in conversion of A-20 and B-25

Air & Sea Museum, Boroko, Papua, New Guinea - Mr. Bruce Roy, Director Narratives from archives
Hell Hole in New Guinea
9th RAAF Operational Group Reports

PHOTOGRAPHS:

Naval Photographic Center, Department of the Navy, Washington, DC (Japanese officers)

National Archives, A/V Section, Washington, DC (Air Force photos)

Australian War Memorial, Photo Section, Canberra City, Australia

3rd Bomb Group History Yearbook

Colonel F.G. Hoffman, Retired (photo of Paul Pappy Gunn)

MAPS AND CHARTS:

Australian War Memorial, Visual Department, Canberra City, Australia

National Archives, A/V Section, U.S. Army maps, Washington DC

MORE THRILLING READING!

McLEANE'S RANGERS
by John Darby

#1: BOUGAINVILLE BREAKOUT   (1207, $2.50)
Even the Marines call on McLeane's Rangers, the toughest,
meanest, and best fighting unit in the Pacific. Their first adventure
pits the Rangers against the entire Japanese garrison in Bougainville. The target—an ammo depot invulnerable to American air
attack . . . and the release of a spy.

#2: TARGET RABAUL   (1271, $2.50)
Rabaul—it was one of the keys to the control of the Pacific and the
Japanese had a lock on it. When nothing else worked, the Allies
called on their most formidable weapon—McLeane's Rangers, the
fearless jungle fighters who didn't know the meaning of the word
quit!

#3: HELL ON HILL 457   (1343, $2.50)
McLeane and his men make a daring parachute drop in the middle
of a heavily fortified Jap position. And the Japs are dug in so deep
in a mountain pass fortress that McLeane may have to blow the
entire pass to rubble—and his men in the bargain!

*Available wherever paperbacks are sold, or order direct from the
Publisher. Send cover price plus 50¢ per copy for mailing and
handling to Zebra Books, 475 Park Avenue South, New York, N.Y.
10016. DO NOT SEND CASH.*